The Open
University

Science: Level 2

S278
EARTH'S PHYSICAL RESOURCES
ORIGIN, USE AND
ENVIRONMENTAL IMPACT

MINERALS
BULK MATERIALS FOR
BUILDING AND INDUSTRY

TOM ARGLES

The S278 Course Team

Chair
Peter Webb

Course Managers
Annemarie Hedges
Jessica Bartlett

Authors
Tom Argles
Kevin Burton
Peter Sheldon
Sandy Smith
Peter Webb

Consultant Author
Mr Kip Jeffrey
(University of Leicester)

Course and Block Assessor
Professor David Manning
(University of Newcastle)

Production Team
Jessica Bartlett (*Indexer*)
Gerry Bearman (*Editor*)
Steve Best (*Graphic artist*)
Kate Bradshaw (*Software designer*)
Roger Courthold (*Graphic artist*)
Rebecca Graham (*Editor*)
Sara Hack (*Graphic artist*)
Liz Lomas (*Course team assistant*)
Judith Pickering (*Project manager*)
Jane Sheppard (*Graphic designer*)
Andy Sutton (*Software designer*)
Pamela Wardell (*Editor*)
Damion Young (*Software designer*)

Acknowledgements

The S278 Course Team gratefully acknowledges the contributions of members of the S268 *Physical Resources and Environment* Course Team (1995) and of its predecessor, S238 *The Earth's Physical Resources* (1984).

This publication forms part of an Open University course S278 *Earth's Physical Resources: Origin, Use and Environmental Impact*. The complete list of texts which make up this course can be found on the back cover. Details of this and other Open University courses can be obtained from the Student Registration and Enquiry Service, The Open University, PO Box 197, Milton Keynes, MK7 6BJ, United Kingdom: tel. +44 (0)870 333 4340, email general-enquiries@open.ac.uk

Alternatively, you may visit the Open University website at http://www.open.ac.uk where you can learn more about the wide range of courses and packs offered at all levels by The Open University.

To purchase a selection of Open University course materials visit http://www.ouw.co.uk, or contact Open University Worldwide, Michael Young Building, Walton Hall, Milton Keynes MK7 6AA, United Kingdom for a brochure: tel. +44 (0)1908 858785; fax +44 (0)1908 858787; email ouwenq@open.ac.uk

The Open University
Walton Hall, Milton Keynes
MK7 6AA

First published 2005, Second edition 2006.

Edited, designed and typeset by The Open University.

Printed and bound in the United Kingdom at the University Press, Cambridge.

ISBN 0 7492 6995 2

2.1

CONTENTS

INTRODUCTION

'Minerals' may conjure up images of colourful chunks of crystal on display in a museum, but in fact we use many minerals — and their derivatives — in our everyday lives, yet we remain largely unaware of their existence. Many are ore minerals, exploited for the metals they contain. This book, however, focuses on the wide range of other minerals and rocks we use, known as **industrial minerals**. Several of these are useful in themselves, like the rock salt used for de-icing roads in winter, while others are a source of useful non-metallic elements: for instance boron obtained from sodium borate is used to make Pyrex™ glass. Industrial minerals may be used on a relatively small scale by specialized industries (e.g. graphite for the thin foil used in particle accelerator experiments), or extracted in bulk for use in construction, as with sand and gravel. Most building materials are low-value bulk commodities requiring minimal processing, whereas some other industrial minerals are very valuable, even before further processing adds more value to the final product. This book is divided into chapters that address each of the main types of industrial minerals in turn.

Figure 1.1 is a simple illustration of the rock cycle. The three main classes of solid rock (igneous, metamorphic and sedimentary) are shown, all of which may be uplifted, weathered and eroded to form loose clastic sediments at the surface (sometimes known collectively as '**drift**' deposits). Included within the

Figure 1.1 Simplified diagram showing how the three main classes of rock (igneous, sedimentary and metamorphic) relate to each other and where rocks and minerals may be obtained from the rock cycle. The numbers in brackets indicate the chapters in which the industrial minerals are described.

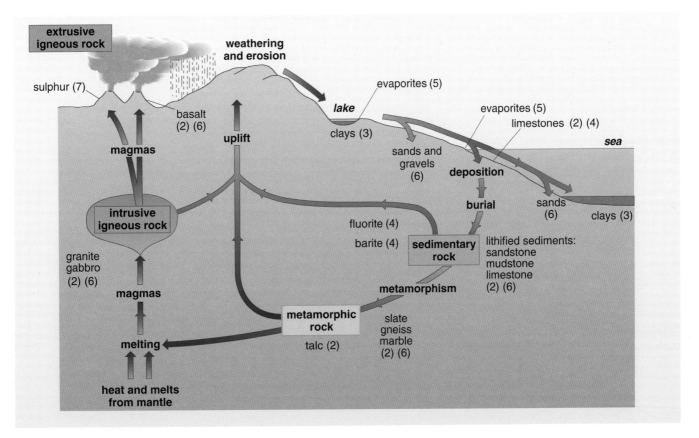

drift are sands and gravels (Chapter 6) and some clays (Chapter 3). Soluble material from weathered rocks ends up in the sea, where it may be precipitated directly to form evaporites such as salt and gypsum (Chapter 5) or used to build shells by marine organisms, whose fragments may accumulate to form limestones (Chapters 2 and 4). Well-lithified or crystalline rocks, generally formed at depth in the crust, may be used as building stone (Chapter 2), or crushed for **aggregate** (Chapter 6). A number of other industrial minerals (e.g. fluorite, talc) are also formed at depth in the crust.

● Where does the majority of industrial mineral extraction take place on Figure 1.1?

○ On or very near the land surface.

● What geological processes raise rocks, such as granite and gneiss, many kilometres up from their sites of formation to the surface where they can be quarried?

○ Tectonic uplift raises the rocks up from depth en masse, while erosion strips off the overlying material. These two combined processes exhume crystalline rocks from deep structural levels.

1.1 Industrial minerals: past and present

1.1.1 Building materials

The use of building materials evolved hand in hand with the gradual change of human society from a nomadic to a sedentary culture. Before Neolithic times (the New Stone Age, which began around 10 000 years ago in Europe and the Near East), there were probably few, if any, permanent settlements. Temporary or seasonal dwellings were made of organic materials (e.g. wood, thatch, mammoth bone, animal hide) and permanent villages only became established when they could be sustained by agriculture. More durable building materials such as sun-dried brick and stone first appeared around 9000 years ago in settlements of the Near and Middle East, such as Jericho. Many of these settlements were partly below ground level, but later on free-standing structures were developed, particularly for buildings with a social or religious significance. The use of resilient natural stone has ensured their survival, leaving us with monuments such as the Pyramids of Egypt, the Great Wall of China, the Standing Stones at Carnac, France, and the Moai of Easter Island. Figure 1.2 locates some of these monuments on a timeline, along with other notable advances in construction.

Box 1.1 reveals the effort involved in building a famous British monument, Stonehenge.

In a modern age where bulk transport is commonplace, it is easy to forget that building materials have traditionally been obtained as close as possible to the building site in order to reduce the effort (and cost) of moving them. In fact, building materials are produced in bulk so cheaply that the cost of transporting them to the market, even a short distance, rapidly exceeds their value at the production site (e.g. a quarry). Such commodities are said to have a high **place value** (i.e. their location is a dominant influence on their cost). In other words, the

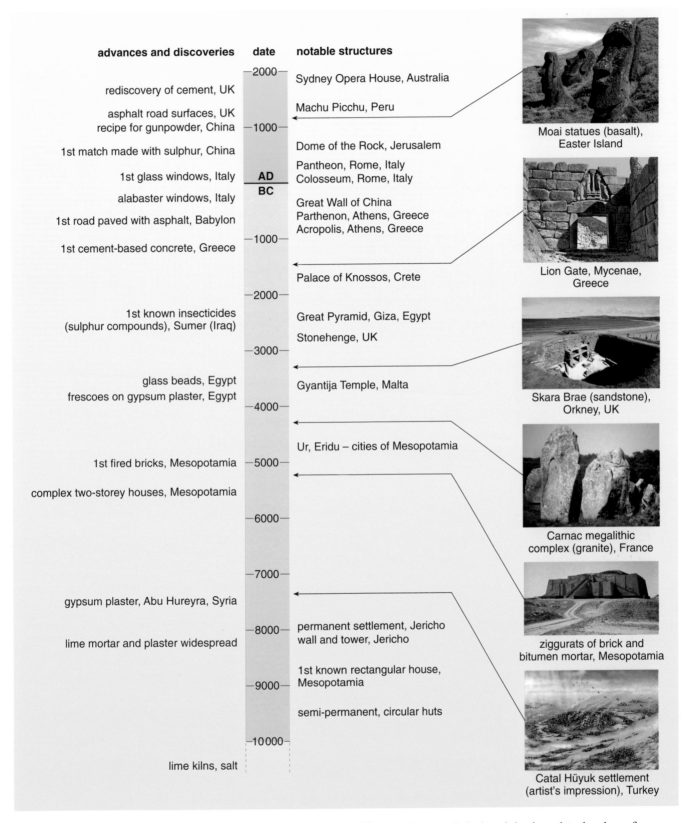

advances and discoveries   **date**   **notable structures**

rediscovery of cement, UK

asphalt road surfaces, UK
recipe for gunpowder, China

1st match made with sulphur, China

1st glass windows, Italy

alabaster windows, Italy

1st road paved with asphalt, Babylon

1st cement-based concrete, Greece

1st known insecticides
(sulphur compounds), Sumer (Iraq)

glass beads, Egypt
frescoes on gypsum plaster, Egypt

1st fired bricks, Mesopotamia

complex two-storey houses, Mesopotamia

gypsum plaster, Abu Hureyra, Syria

lime mortar and plaster widespread

lime kilns, salt

—2000—
—1000—
AD
BC
—1000—
—2000—
—3000—
—4000—
—5000—
—6000—
—7000—
—8000—
—9000—
—10 000—

Sydney Opera House, Australia

Machu Picchu, Peru

Dome of the Rock, Jerusalem

Pantheon, Rome, Italy
Colosseum, Rome, Italy

Great Wall of China
Parthenon, Athens, Greece
Acropolis, Athens, Greece

Palace of Knossos, Crete

Great Pyramid, Giza, Egypt

Stonehenge, UK

Gyantija Temple, Malta

Ur, Eridu – cities of Mesopotamia

permanent settlement, Jericho
wall and tower, Jericho

1st known rectangular house,
Mesopotamia

semi-permanent, circular huts

Moai statues (basalt),
Easter Island

Lion Gate, Mycenae,
Greece

Skara Brae (sandstone),
Orkney, UK

Carnac megalithic
complex (granite), France

ziggurats of brick and
bitumen mortar, Mesopotamia

Catal Hüyuk settlement
(artist's impression), Turkey

Figure 1.2   Timeline locating selected constructions and significant advances in industrial mineral technology from around 10 000 years BC to the present day.

Box 1.1   Lessons from Stonehenge

Like Carnac in Brittany, France, the building of Stonehenge on the chalk downland of Salisbury Plain, England, represents a monumental achievement for the time. Earthworks at the site date from about 3000 BC, but it is the assembly of the huge sandstone blocks (sarsens) and smaller bluestones (mainly types of dolerite, with some volcanic rocks and sandstones) from about 2500 BC to 1900 BC that stirs fascination and provokes questions.

There were originally two groups of sarsens: a circle of 30 upright stones weighing around 25 tonnes each (linked by lintels), and an inner horseshoe of five trilithons (pairs of upright sarsens topped by a lintel). The heaviest sarsen weighs about 45 tonnes. Though commonly described as 'local', the nearest identifiable source for the sarsens is the Marlborough Downs, about 30 km to the north of Salisbury Plain. It has been estimated that 500 men would be needed to haul a single stone on a sledge with leather ropes, and another 100 men to place rollers in front of the sledge — a gruelling overland journey with 25 tonnes of sandstone.

Before the sarsens were moved to the site, however, about 80 smaller bluestones (each weighing about 4 tonnes) were erected. Research by workers at The Open University has confirmed the source of the bluestones to be the Preseli Mountains of southwest Wales, which are over 200 km away from Stonehenge. No wonder legends attribute their transportation to Merlin's magic! Some scholars have argued that the stones were carried by an ancient glacier, but it is often suggested that they were transported by people, perhaps following the route shown in Figure 1.3. This route, though considerably further than the direct overland route, takes advantage of the relative ease of transporting cumbersome goods by water (sea and river). Transporting bulk materials by sea remains important right up to the present day.

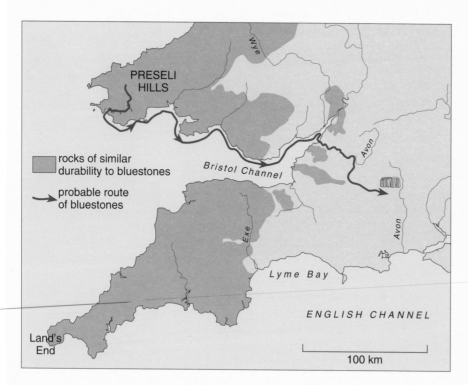

Figure 1.3   Probable route along which the bluestones were taken from the Preseli Mountains to Stonehenge.

lower the value of building stone at the quarry gate, the *higher* its place value. We discuss place value in more detail in Section 2.3.2.

Ancient monuments (such as those listed above) suggest that natural stone was the premier building material for millennia, and prized for its durability. Throughout history, however, stone has generally been the most costly bulk material both to quarry and to process for use in construction, so people tended to adapt cheaper materials for everyday buildings — for instance wood, or clay as daub or for bricks. The modern, industrialized world requires vast quantities of cheap building materials for roads, urban development and simply bulk 'fill'. Fortunately, many materials (e.g. sand, gravel, clay) occur at or just below the land surface. Since production of **dressed stone** (regular blocks produced by cutting and chiselling) incurs high labour costs, it is more cost-effective to convert these unconsolidated sediments into materials like brick or concrete that match the strength and hardness of stone rather than use dressed stone. In many modern buildings, these cheap substitutes for stone, along with steel, form the basic shell, whereas thin, polished sheets of decorative stone (e.g. granite or marble) are used as cladding to present an impressive (and expensive) corporate or civic exterior.

From Neolithic times, two other industrial minerals, lime (roasted limestone) and gypsum, were mixed with sand and water as **mortars** to lay masonry blocks or bricks, and used in plaster (frescoes from the Egyptian pyramids through to the Sistine Chapel in Rome were crafted on gypsum plaster). Bitumen (a natural mixture of hydrocarbons, sometimes called tar) was used in place of mortar in the ziggurats of Mesopotamia around 5000 BC, while the earliest recorded road paved with **asphalt** (tar mixed with crushed rock) was built in Babylon between 625 BC and 604 BC, over 1000 years before Sir Walter Raleigh 'discovered' the tar lake at La Brea in Trinidad.

1.1.2 Other industrial minerals

Several metals (gold, silver, copper, iron, tin, mercury) were known to humankind from prehistoric times, and this is also true of some industrial minerals (e.g. lime, salt; Figure 1.2). Sulphur, perhaps because it occurs as a native element on volcanoes, is one example. Its combustibility lent it a variety of uses at least 4000 years ago, for instance as medicine and incense, as well as for fumigation and bleaching. Chinese alchemists gradually developed mixtures using sulphur from 150 AD to 1040 AD, when the first recipe for true gunpowder was written down; the first matches were sulphur-impregnated sticks developed in China in 577 AD. But it was the recognition of the versatility of sulphuric acid in 18th-century Europe that sparked the huge increase in demand for sulphur. In contrast to sulphur, native graphite was not discovered until around 1500 AD, in the English Lake District. Glass windows were rare — and costly — until the end of the 17th century, although the first known artificial glass dates from almost 4000 BC; the Romans used thin plates of gypsum (alabaster) for temple windows instead. However, perhaps the most familiar industrial mineral, salt, is also the one with the longest history (Box 1.2).

Most resources that we extract from the inorganic world are, like salt, selected for their *chemical composition* — for the metal they contain, or their fuel content, or other elements needed for industry or agriculture. Building materials differ in that it is dominantly their *physical and mechanical* properties that are important.

Box 1.2   Salt for all seasons

Common salt (NaCl) is biologically necessary to sustain human life. The great early civilizations in Africa, the Middle East, China, and India all developed on the fringes of arid zones around natural salt deposits — rather than in humid northern Europe where surface salt deposits simply dissolve. Its poor potential for preservation means that the earliest evidence for the use of salt is in a Chinese treatise on pharmacology, written around 2700 BC; however, other linguistic references show that salt was a vital part of the religious, economic and social fabric of all early societies. Domestication of animals would not have been possible without salt supplements to their diet, and it was associated with fertility in many cultures. At the same time, the Egyptians used it in mummification! Salt cakes were used as currency in ancient Ethiopia, and Marco Polo found that similar cakes stamped with the seal of Kublai Khan served the same purpose during the 13th century in Tibet. Roman soldiers were given a salt ration known as *salarium argentum*, from which the English word 'salary' is derived. On the other side of the coin, taxes have been levied on salt by governments from ancient China and Rome to France during the 1940s; although an earlier salt tax in France was repealed during the French Revolution, it was revived by Napoleon to finance his military campaigns.

Politically, salt exerted a huge influence, conferring immense power on those who controlled its supply or trade, such as the Doges of Venice, the Habsburgs in Austria and the Archbishops of Salzburg. Salt works (notably at Saltville, Virginia) were targeted by both sides in the American War of Independence, because salt was vital for preserving food to supply the armies. It is easy to forget, in a society with refrigeration, freeze-drying, canning and rapid bulk transport, how important salt was for preservation until relatively recently, particularly in fuelling the age of exploration.

The production of salt through the ages follows a distinctive pattern — from surface gathering, to mining, and on to manufacture. Initially, salt crystals were simply 'harvested' from natural inland or coastal saltpans (Figure 1.4), a technique known as 'dragging and gathering' by the ancient Chinese. This activity probably dated back to before 6000 BC. With increasing demand, subsurface salt deposits were mined. Around 1000 BC in Austria, galleries were driven 400 m into the mountainside to extract salt, since surface deposits were already exhausted. By 400 AD in China, salt deposits at depth were being drilled using bamboo pipes and pumped water, a method that is essentially unchanged in many modern production plants. Although solar evaporation in pans continues to this day, the use of fuel to accelerate the evaporation of brine in clay vessels is recorded in China around 800 BC, and the cost of fuel entered the salt equation. In the latter years of the 20th century, concern about the consequences of fuel consumption prompted a marked return to harnessing solar power alone for simple evaporation of brine.

Figure 1.4   The 'dragging and gathering' method of harvesting salt from artificial saltpans, Thailand.

For instance, materials for modern road surfaces must be able to bear heavy loads, drain efficiently, and be resistant to both skidding and wear from tyres as well as to frost damage.

Question 1.1

What physical properties *apart from* load-bearing strength would be particularly important for the following applications?

(a) The brick lining of a blast furnace.

(b) The roof of a house in Greenland.

(c) A deceleration lane at a busy road junction.

(d) Granite cladding on the facade of an exclusive hotel.

As many building materials are cheap and bulky, they have a high place value, and are extracted close to their markets. Since most countries have abundant reserves of building materials, imports and exports are low relative to domestic consumption. International trade is more important for many other industrial minerals because of their patchy worldwide distribution; they also tend to be more valuable and less bulky to transport than materials used in construction. Table 1.1 contains production figures (in 10^3 tonnes) for the year 2001 for some building materials and industrial minerals, both in global terms and in four separate countries.

●   Almost 400 times more cement than fluorspar was produced globally in 2001. Suggest two important reasons for this.

○   The main reason is *demand* (cement is produced in bulk for the construction industry, whereas fluorspar is used in smaller quantities mainly for the chemical industry and for smelting). The second reason is the relative *natural abundance* of each of these resources (cement is produced from widespread bulk materials (limestones and clays), whereas fluorspar occurs mainly in small vein deposits).

Table 1.1   Global and national production of some construction and industrial materials for the year 2001.

Material	World/10^3 t	China/10^3 t	India/10^3 t	UK/10^3 t	USA/10^3 t
barite	6 700	3 600	850	66	400
cement	1 700 000	626 500	100 000	11 854	90 450
kaolin	44 100	600	710	2 200	8 110
gypsum	104 000	6 800	2 250	1 700	16 300
lime	118 000	22 000	320	2 500	18 900
potash	26 400	385	0	882	1 200
salt	225 000	31 000	14 500	6 100	44 800
sand and gravel	unknown	unknown	unknown	101 397	1 130 000
fluorspar	4 530	2 450	900	50	0
sulphur	57 300	5 380	941	111	9 250
talc	8 920	3 500	546	5	853

These figures highlight the contrast between construction materials and other industrial minerals; in fact the vast amounts of building materials produced in most countries are not accurately known. Gypsum and lime are produced in intermediate quantities, reflecting their use in construction (gypsum) and agriculture (lime), as well as smaller amounts used in specialized applications.

1.2 Industrial minerals nearer home

The quantity of gypsum produced globally every year may seem vast, but a typical 3-bedroomed house in Europe contains up to six tonnes of gypsum (mainly in plasterboard). What other building materials make up an average house in a developed country — or indeed your own home?

Figure 1.5 matches some physical resources to parts of a typical 3-bedroomed house in the UK; in later chapters you will learn more about how these resources have progressed from extraction to final product. Rough quantities of some industrial minerals used to build an 'average' family home in the UK are given on the figure. Other major materials might include:

- wood — for joists, frames, doors;
- plastic — for frames, pipes, guttering;
- water — for mixing cement and plaster.

Up to four tonnes of ash recovered from coal-fired power stations may even be mixed with cement to make lightweight blocks for the inner walls.

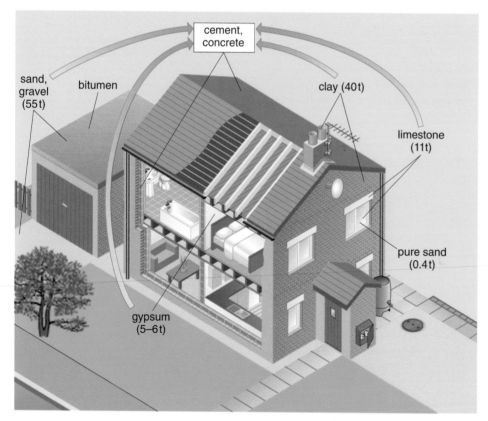

Figure 1.5 Selected components of a typical modern house matched to the physical resources used in their production. Approximate amounts of the industrial minerals used in its construction are also shown.

Not all dwellings are constructed in such a complex manner: the world has a huge variety of building materials as well as brick and concrete (Figure 1.6). Some derive from physical resources (mud, corrugated iron, ice), but many are based on organic materials (timber, straw, grass, animal hide, wool, paper, cardboard). These materials reflect several factors, including availability of resources (Tibetan yurts, adobe huts, igloos); nomadic lifestyle (Native American tepees, thatch huts); and even tectonic environment — traditional houses in Japan, with paper walls, were safer during earthquakes than more robust buildings (and easy to rebuild). However, buildings made of inorganic, physical resources tend to be the most enduring. The next chapter explores perhaps the most durable of these materials: natural stone.

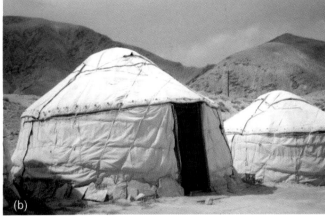

Figure 1.6 Examples illustrating the variety of building materials used worldwide. (a) Adobe houses, New Mexico, USA. Well adapted to an arid climate, the thick mud walls absorb heat during the day, and re-radiate it at night, regulating the temperature inside the house. (b) Tibetan yurt made of woven yak's wool. Wood is scarce in Tibet, and these tents are ideally suited to a nomadic lifestyle. (c) Inuit igloo, another example of ingenious use of available resources. Igloos were mainly temporary seasonal shelters. (d) Experimental school constructed using cardboard, Westborough, UK. Cardboard was used to provide relief housing quickly after an earthquake in Kobe, Japan, in 1995.

1.3   Summary of Chapter 1

1   Industrial minerals can be subdivided into materials used for building, which are generally low-value bulk commodities, and those used, typically in smaller quantities, in other, more specialized industries.

2   Evolution of sedentary cultures around 10 000 years ago was the catalyst for more widespread use of physical resources (mud bricks and stone) as building materials. Construction of durable, free-standing buildings spread from the Near and Middle East (e.g. Jericho, Mesopotamia) throughout Western Europe.

3   Only the most important religious or social constructions could command the huge effort (and workforce) required to build such ambitious and enduring structures. In the case of Stonehenge, around eighty bluestone blocks were transported at least 200 km from southwest Wales.

4   Most building materials are extracted in bulk from deposits close to the surface, and their high place value means they are generally transported only short distances to their markets. Processing (e.g. cutting and polishing granite slabs) adds value to some building materials.

5   Most countries have abundant reserves of building materials, but many industrial minerals are unevenly distributed across the world, making international trade important.

6   Construction materials are valued mainly for their physical and mechanical properties. Many other industrial minerals, however, are exploited for their chemical properties or constituents (e.g. salt, sulphur).

7   Even in the modern world, a huge variety of resources, many of them of organic origin, are used for building. This variety reflects the physical and economic environment of specific localities. In industrialized nations, a wide range of physical resources may be used in a single house.

NATURAL BUILDING STONE

This chapter explores building with stone, from the nature and origins of the rocks themselves, through their extraction and economic context, to the impact of their exploitation on the environment.

2.1 The geological context of building stones

2.1.1 Foundations of the landscape

Many building materials are derived from the loose sedimentary material (drift) at the Earth's surface, which results from chemical and mechanical weathering of the solid rock underneath. If this drift layer were stripped off, the various types of bedrock beneath would be exposed: these correspond to the units shown on most geological maps. It is perhaps no accident that Britain was the cradle of the science of geology because a wide variety of rock types and geological structures are on show within a comparatively small area. However, even Britain had to wait until 1815 for the first published detailed geological map (of England and Wales), drawn by a surveyor called William Smith from his work on the canal network.

- What was the major geological factor that restricted mapping of the bedrock prior to this?

- Various types of superficial deposit, or drift, masked the bedrock geology throughout much of the UK, especially in southern Britain.

It was only after the widespread excavation of canal channels and railway cuttings that geologists were able to peer through the drift and map the outcrops of bedrock underneath. The bedrock was important both as a source of ores and fuel to feed the Industrial Revolution, and as a source of building stones, or mudstones (clays, shales) for bricks, for the burgeoning population. Thus the Geological Survey was set up in 1835 to map the bedrock. In recent times, the Survey has been re-mapping the drift, reflecting the increase in the relative importance of superficial deposits for construction (and the simultaneous decline in the UK ore-based industry). An example of each type of map is shown in Figure 2.1 (overleaf). These maps illustrate the extensive coverage of drift, which is typical of much of Britain.

Almost all natural building stones are extracted from bedrock, then dressed to form blocks of the desired dimensions — in fact, such dressed stone is usually known as '**dimension stone**'. Only where drift contains abundant, large boulders (such as glacial moraines in the Himalayas) does it provide building stone directly, in some cases with no dressing at all. Walls of village houses in the valleys of northern Pakistan are commonly constructed from such local, rounded glacial boulders. For the more important buildings in the village, the largest boulders are dynamited to provide an abundance of easily dressed fragments.

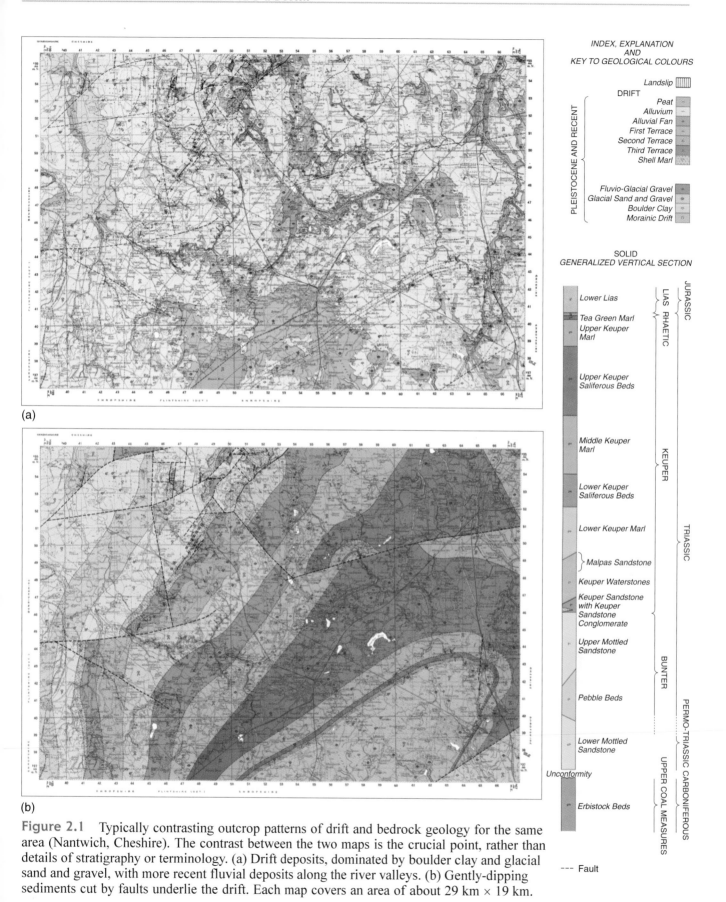

Figure 2.1 Typically contrasting outcrop patterns of drift and bedrock geology for the same area (Nantwich, Cheshire). The contrast between the two maps is the crucial point, rather than details of stratigraphy or terminology. (a) Drift deposits, dominated by boulder clay and glacial sand and gravel, with more recent fluvial deposits along the river valleys. (b) Gently-dipping sediments cut by faults underlie the drift. Each map covers an area of about 29 km × 19 km.

● Suggest why the more important buildings in the village tend to be built in this way, while poorer dwellings use rounded boulders.

○ Prestige buildings can justify the extra expense of using dynamite and the cost of the labour involved in dressing the stone fragments.

For now, the drift can be ignored while we concentrate on the potential building stones underneath (we will return to the drift in Chapter 6). In Britain, there is a broad shift from young, softer rock strata in the south and east to older, more resistant, crystalline rocks in the highland areas of the north and west. The older rocks are typically highly deformed (folded and faulted), whereas those of the south and east are structurally fairly simple, with gently dipping beds. Much of this contrast is due to the distribution of the main three rock types in the UK: sedimentary rocks dominate the south and east, while the north and west are underlain mainly by a complex mixture of igneous and metamorphic rocks.

2.1.2 Rock properties

The shapes and sizes of the grains in igneous, metamorphic and sedimentary rocks (Figures 2.2 and 2.3) influence their textures and reflect how they formed in their part of the rock cycle (Figure 1.1). Igneous rocks, crystallizing from a liquid magma, develop a strong, interlocking network of mineral grains as they cool. Generally speaking, the quicker an igneous rock cools, the finer the crystals. Alignment of crystals is relatively rare in igneous rocks, whereas many metamorphic rocks have a strong preferred orientation of grains caused by directed stress (pressure) at depth in the crust. The crystals in metamorphic rocks form by the replacement of pre-existing mineral grains by new minerals at high temperatures and pressures during burial. Consequently, metamorphic rocks also have an interlocking, crystalline structure, with crystals tending to be coarser the deeper they are buried (i.e. the higher the temperature and pressure).

Figure 2.2 Typical textures of: (a and b) igneous, (c) metamorphic and (d) sedimentary rocks in hand specimen. (a) Polished granite with interlocking crystals from Shap, Cumbria. (b) Basalt, a fine-grained igneous rock that cooled more quickly than (a), with a reddish weathering crust. (c) Mica schist, composed of aligned, interlocking crystals of different minerals; this alignment imparts a characteristic planar fabric (or cleavage) to the rock. (d) Triassic sandstone, containing mostly rounded grains of quartz cemented together with reddish haematite. The cm-scale subtle colour banding represents sedimentary bedding.

The majority of sedimentary rocks are composed of the weathered fragments of rocks that have been eroded and transported by water, wind and/or ice and subsequently deposited in layers. Whereas crystal shape in crystalline rocks is mainly dictated by the type of mineral, sedimentary grains typically reflect the degree of abrasion they have experienced during transport, which tends to make them more rounded. The grain size of a sedimentary rock is mainly determined by the conditions prevailing during its deposition: quiet lakes deposit very fine sediments, whereas stormy beaches are dominated by pebbles.

The layers or beds in which sediments are laid down are an example of the many structures that occur in rocks. The mineral alignment fabric (known as cleavage) that allows metamorphic slate to be split easily into sheets is another example, but this is caused by deformation of the rock. Other structures arising from the stresses placed on rocks in the crust include folds, and cracks such as joints or faults. Rocks devoid of any such flaws have always been prized for carving, as they can be worked equally easily in all directions. Such rocks are known as **freestones**.

(a)

Far from being one of a million shades of grey, rocks have an infinite variety of hues, imparted by their different chemical compositions and mineralogy. Further variety arises because they may become stained during chemical attack at the Earth's surface (weathering). A russet colour is commonly due to staining by iron oxides — a kind of 'natural rust' (Figure 2.2b). Some rocks are highly prized as ornamental stones, primarily on the basis of their attractive colour and patterning.

Hardness and durability are important properties for building stone. Two common rocks, sandstone and limestone, are mainly composed of the minerals quartz and calcite respectively, whose contrasting properties affect the character of the whole rock. A steel knife will easily scratch the softer calcite, but will make no impression on hard quartz. Quartz is also chemically resistant, whereas calcite is easily corroded by dilute acid such as lemon juice (citric acid), or even rainwater, which is naturally slightly acidic. In consequence, quartz-rich sandstones are tough and durable; by contrast, limestones, and sandstones containing calcite, tend to corrode and crumble over time. Most crystalline igneous and metamorphic rocks are relatively tough and durable due to the minerals they contain. Exceptions include some metamorphic schists that contain a high proportion of the very soft mineral talc. (Talc is a useful industrial mineral in its own right — see Box 2.1.)

(b)

(c)

Figure 2.3 Typical textures of (a and b) igneous, (c) metamorphic and (d) sedimentary rocks under the microscope. Field of view: 4 mm in all cases. (a) Gabbro with characteristic interlocking crystals and no visible voids; the coarse crystals indicate slow cooling and crystallization. (b) Basalt, a fine-grained equivalent of gabbro that cooled more quickly. (c) Mica schist, composed of interlocking crystals of different minerals, most of which are aligned by directed stress during burial and deformation. (In this specimen, brown biotite flakes are wrapped around a large garnet crystal.) This alignment imparts a characteristic planar fabric (or cleavage) to the rock. (d) Partially cemented quartz sandstone; detrital quartz grains have been glued together in places with silica cement deposited in between them, though there is still a significant proportion of voids (dark blue) in the rock.

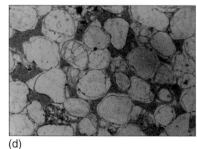
(d)

Box 2.1 Talc — metamorphism's soft touch

The heat and pressure imposed on metamorphic rocks deep in the Earth's crust typically produces hard, crystalline rocks — but one exception is soapstone (Figure 2.4a), a metamorphic rock rich in the mineral talc ($Mg_3Si_4O_{10}(OH)_2$). In fact, talc is one of the softest minerals of all, feeling greasy to the touch. The atoms in talc are arranged in sheets that are only weakly bound together, and can slide past each other easily. Stacks of these sheets form larger plates (Figure 2.4b) that allow talc to act as a lubricant, leaving the skin feeling smooth after application. These sheets also mix more easily with organic liquids than with water, so talc blends well with organic binders, solvents, oils and resins.

Talc is generally formed, along with other minerals, when a magnesium-rich rock is heavily altered by reaction with a hot fluid passing through it. Deposits vary widely in talc content, plate size, colour, associated minerals, and physical properties. The purest white talc is formed from dolomitic (Mg-rich) or siliceous marbles.

World production of talc (including soapstone) is around 8.9 Mt per year [1 Mt (megatonne) = 10^6 t (tonnes)]. China is the world's largest producer, followed by the USA, India and Brazil. Production in Europe is dominated by Finland and France. The UK has some deposits, mainly in Shetland, which have been worked in the past. Most talc is extracted from open pits, but there are underground talc mines as well.

Talc rock is commonly powdered for use in a range of products. The key properties for most applications are softness, relative inertness, a white colour, and water repellency. Being relatively inert, talc is used widely as a **filler** (e.g. to bulk out paints and paper), and as a 'carrier' for the tiny amounts of drug in pharmaceutical tablets that would otherwise be inconveniently small. It also acts as a thickener in paints, improving the covering and adhesion properties. Strangely for such a soft mineral, the platy structure imparts optimum rigidity and impact strength to plastics, which are useful properties for car bumpers and food packaging, for example. Plastic garden furniture may contain anything up to 20% talc as filler. Laboratory worktops requiring both rigidity and resistance to acid, heat and electricity commonly contain talc.

Its most familiar use, in talcum powder, demands high-quality talc and is a relatively minor application, particularly as many baby powders now also contain finely ground calcium carbonate (limestone). Wax crayons containing talc for smoother spreading were actually boycotted by customers in the USA during public health scares when some fibrous minerals similar to 'asbestos' were identified in the talc deposits. Such tiny quantities occurred in the products that the risk of inhaling fibres was miniscule, but it illustrates an important point regarding public perception of safety. Media scares can produce a drastic shift in consumer confidence, despite the best efforts of scientists to reassure the public, and such scares have led to the closure of mines.

(a)

5 µm

(b)

Figure 2.4 (a) The softness of soapstone has been exploited for centuries for carving ornaments, such as this incense burner. (b) Scanning electron microscope (SEM) image of platy talc crystals.

Many volcanic ash deposits are too soft for building; yet the popular slates of the English Lake District were once volcanic ash too, during the Ordovician Period (around 450 Ma ago). This illustrates a useful rule of thumb: the older a rock is, the more likely it is to be tough enough for building. The reason for this is that a rock with a long history is more likely to have been deeply buried and thus subjected to the effects of heat, pressure and fluids, which combine to harden or 'lithify' the rock material. This is particularly true of rocks originally deposited at the Earth's surface, such as volcanic ash, or indeed any other sediment. Because many sediments are composed of individual particles (grains of sand or clay, plant or shell fragments etc.), there are initially gaps between them that are filled with water or air. These pores are very useful for storing water and oil, but undesirable in a building material because they tend to weaken the rock. **Porosity** is a measure of the proportion of voids in a material, generally expressed as a percentage:

$$\text{porosity} = \frac{\text{volume of space}}{\text{total volume}} \times 100\% \tag{2.1}$$

Porous rocks can suffer from frost damage if they become soaked with water and then frozen, especially if the mineral grains are poorly cemented. When water in the pores turns to ice, it expands. This may cause the rock to split, and in extreme cases it becomes a crumbling mass of fragments — an undesirable tendency in a building material.

Modern building materials are subjected to rigorous quantitative tests to determine their porosity. A simple qualitative method to test porosity is to half immerse a rock in water: porous and permeable materials allow water to be drawn up well above the water level in which they are standing, just as spilled tea is drawn up into a sugar cube.

There are very few voids in crystalline igneous or metamorphic rocks because these rocks were formed by crystals of minerals growing together into an interlocking matrix (Figure 2.3). Lithification of sediments involves the closure of voids by compaction during burial, combined with their infill by natural mineral cements. This process of cementation involves dissolution of material such as silica (SiO_2) or calcium carbonate ($CaCO_3$) from the sedimentary particles, followed by reprecipitation of the same material in the voids (Figure 2.5).

A simple experiment with sugar demonstrates how loose sand can be cemented to form a sedimentary rock. Dry sugar behaves rather like loose sand. But if you add a few drops of water to a bowl of sugar and let it dry thoroughly over several hours, solid lumps will form.

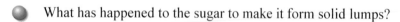 What has happened to the sugar to make it form solid lumps?

Water seeping into the spaces between the grains dissolves some sugar from the surfaces of the grains. As the water evaporates, the sugar in the solution crystallizes onto the remaining grains, forming a coating that cements them together.

With time, groundwater can act in a similar way on sediments to produce extremely tough, non-porous rock, such as the Carboniferous limestone of northern England which is used extensively in road-building (Chapter 6). In fact,

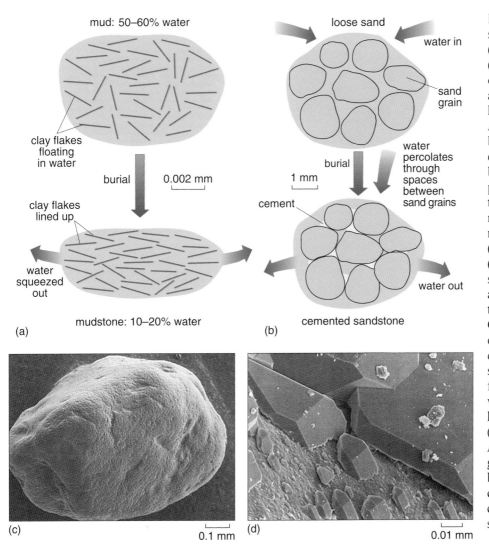

Figure 2.5 From loose sediment to sedimentary rock: (a) from mud to mudstone (compaction) — the small flakes of clay minerals are originally almost 'floating' in pore water held in a loose clay deposit. As compaction proceeds, they become squashed together, thus expelling a lot of water, and become lined up to be nearly parallel to each other by the time the original mud has become a mudstone or shale. Very little mineral cement is deposited. (b) From sand to sandstone (cementation): grains of quartz support each other in loose sand, and only squash down a little due to the weight of overlying rocks. Grains become attached to each other as quartz cement is deposited between the grains, some of this cement having come from dissolution of the grains where they touch, a process known as pressure solution. (c) A sand grain from the Saudi Arabian Desert, well rounded by grain-to-grain impacts (sand blasting). (d) Aligned quartz crystals growing as a cement coating on the rough surface of a sandstone grain.

most of the traditional building stones in the UK are sedimentary, rather than igneous or metamorphic rocks. This is because the sedimentary rocks tend to occur in simple, gently inclined layers that are easily quarried. In addition, sedimentary rocks tend to be easier to dress, carve and lay than crystalline igneous or metamorphic rocks.

2.2 Sources of stone

2.2.1 Vernacular architecture

Because stone for building was traditionally quarried locally and not transported far, many regions have a distinct character, known as 'vernacular architecture', derived from their own particular local building stone, such as granite in Cornwall or limestone in the Cotswolds. What is your local building stone? You may find it along with your local vernacular architecture in older buildings — farms, churches and inns for example; otherwise you may be able to deduce what it is from a geological map (e.g. Figure 2.6).

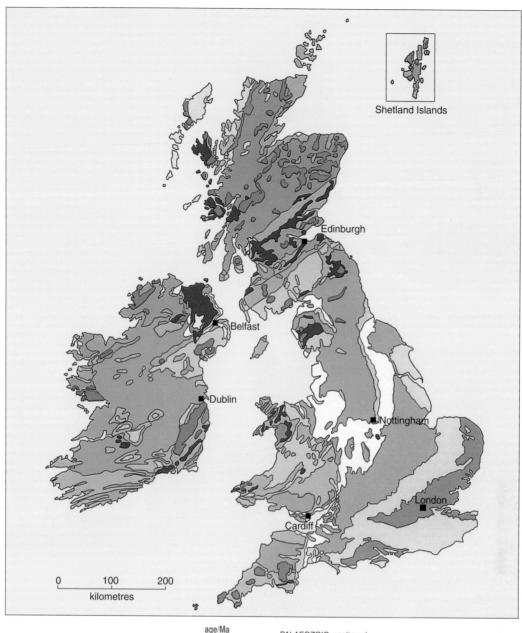

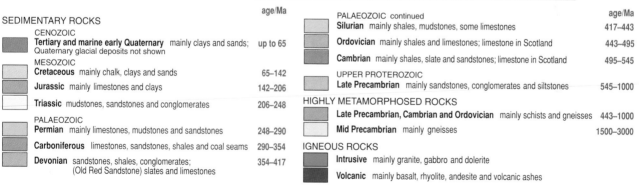

SEDIMENTARY ROCKS	age/Ma
CENOZOIC	
Tertiary and marine early Quaternary mainly clays and sands; Quaternary glacial deposits not shown	up to 65
MESOZOIC	
Cretaceous mainly chalk, clays and sands	65–142
Jurassic mainly limestones and clays	142–206
Triassic mudstones, sandstones and conglomerates	206–248
PALAEOZOIC	
Permian mainly limestones, mudstones and sandstones	248–290
Carboniferous limestones, sandstones, shales and coal seams	290–354
Devonian sandstones, shales, conglomerates; (Old Red Sandstone) slates and limestones	354–417

PALAEOZOIC continued	age/Ma
Silurian mainly shales, mudstones, some limestones	417–443
Ordovician mainly shales and limestones; limestone in Scotland	443–495
Cambrian mainly shales, slate and sandstones; limestone in Scotland	495–545
UPPER PROTEROZOIC	
Late Precambrian mainly sandstones, conglomerates and siltstones	545–1000
HIGHLY METAMORPHOSED ROCKS	
Late Precambrian, Cambrian and Ordovician mainly schists and gneisses	443–1000
Mid Precambrian mainly gneisses	1500–3000
IGNEOUS ROCKS	
Intrusive mainly granite, gabbro and dolerite	
Volcanic mainly basalt, rhyolite, andesite and volcanic ashes	

Figure 2.6 Geological map of Britain and Ireland. (BD/IPR/7-14 British Geological Survey. © NERC all rights reserved.)

Question 2.1

Use the geological map of the British Isles (Figure 2.6) to answer the following:

(a) Give the locations on the map of the following: (i) the youngest (most recent) strata; (ii) the southernmost outcrop of Precambrian sediments; (iii) the southernmost outcrop of intrusive igneous rock.

(b) What is the difference in age between the strata underlying London and Dublin, and which is more likely to be suitable for use as a building stone?

(c) A journey in a straight line from London to Edinburgh has been called 'a journey back through time'. How far north (in kilometres) do you have to go on that line to reach rock strata that are older than: (i) 65 Ma; (ii) 290 Ma; (iii) 443 Ma?

(d) How far north from London do you have to go on the same journey to reach an outcrop of igneous rock? What can you deduce about the age of these intrusive igneous rocks?

Some of central and northern England is underlain by a red sandstone laid down in desert conditions during the Permian and Triassic Periods (206–290 Ma). Known as 'Penrith sandstone' in northern England, it is a freestone that has been widely used for building (Figure 2.7a), and being made mainly of silica it does not corrode as easily as limestone. Where suitable building stone is lacking, as in southeast England, broken flints have often been used to face buildings (as in Figure 2.7b).

Figure 2.7 Examples of vernacular architecture.
(a) Permian sandstone, Penrith, Cumbria. Dressed blocks of red Penrith sandstone have been used for the lintels and cornerstones, with paler, roughly dressed Carboniferous sandstones used for the bulk of the walls. The building stands on an exposure of cross-bedded Penrith sandstone (lower right).

(b) Flint used to give a black and white geometric effect, Stow-on-the-Wold, Gloucestershire. The honey-coloured blocks are Jurassic limestone; the smooth weathered surfaces of the flint pebbles are white, and the freshly broken interiors are black.

2.2.2 Jurassic limestones in England

The soft, creamy beige-coloured limestones so typical of Cotswold villages (Figure 2.8a) occur in a narrow outcrop of Jurassic age (~ 170 Ma) that stretches from the Portland area of Dorset to North Yorkshire (Figure 2.6). Most are oolitic, with many tiny spherical grains looking rather like fish roe. When well-cemented, as in some of the limestones found around Bath and Portland, they are excellent freestones. The City of Bath is dominated by Bath stone, while white Portland stone has been used both throughout Britain (Figure 2.8b) and abroad since Inigo Jones and Christopher Wren used it in the rebuilding of London (notably in St Paul's Cathedral) after the Great Fire in 1666. Impressive Portland stone buildings can be found from Belfast to New Delhi, and crosses and headstones marking graves in war cemeteries worldwide are of Portland stone. Jurassic limestone is in demand for restoration work, since many of the original limestones chosen for buildings are porous and have been attacked by acid rain (e.g. Houses of Parliament, London).

Figure 2.8 Examples of Jurassic limestone architecture: (a) Oolitic limestone in a Cotswold village, including a drystone wall and roof 'slates' of thinly-bedded Jurassic limestone (known as Stonesfield Slate); (b) Stockport Town Hall, built 1904–8, in the 'wedding cake' style by Sir Brumwell Thomas, who built a similar one in Belfast. The rock is white Portland stone.

(a)

(b)

Box 2.2   Stones for a colony: South Australia

From the early days of colonization, natural stone has been used extensively for building in South Australia (Figure 2.9a). Initially, this was because wood was scarce in the state; now stone from South Australia is exported worldwide. Despite substitution by modern materials such as concrete, steel and glass, building stones still dominate in many urban areas, including central Adelaide. This is due not only to the preservation of older buildings in the traditional materials (Figure 2.9b), but also to the almost exclusive use of local stones for polished slabs to face modern buildings. Since the 1960s, there has also been a general upsurge of interest in using natural stone in both the domestic and commercial sectors.

The earliest quarries, opened in the 1840s, were worked predominately by Cornish miners from Britain for slate and 'bluestone', a local term for siltstones of Precambrian age (these sedimentary 'bluestones' are different from the igneous bluestones used in

Stonehenge (Box 1.1)). Trade was soon brisk, with slate shipped out to other parts of Australia. In 1891, two ships per week, each carrying 20 000 roofing slates, were loaded up using teams of bullocks, and sailed from Port Adelaide. In the 1860s, larger civic buildings, such as the Town Hall, were built mainly of local sandstone. This tough stone was also important for domestic construction into the 20th century. Granite and marble were also used, particularly for prestigious buildings: Parliament House presents an impressive front of Kapunda marble columns on a base of granite quarried from near Victor Harbour.

It was not only ancient rocks that were used; the arid climate causes lithification of the soil in many parts of the state, forming a limestone called 'calcrete'. This superficial deposit, known locally as 'paddock limestone', was used widely for building by the early settlers, especially in areas remote from other sources of building stone.

In the early 21st century, sandstone and slate are still important materials in the construction industry — and elsewhere (Mintaro slate is used for billiard tables). Half of South Australia's production of dimension stone in the late 1990s was limestone. However, many igneous rocks (mainly granites) are finding markets in Southeast Asia, Japan, Europe and North America as ornamental stone (Figure 2.9c).

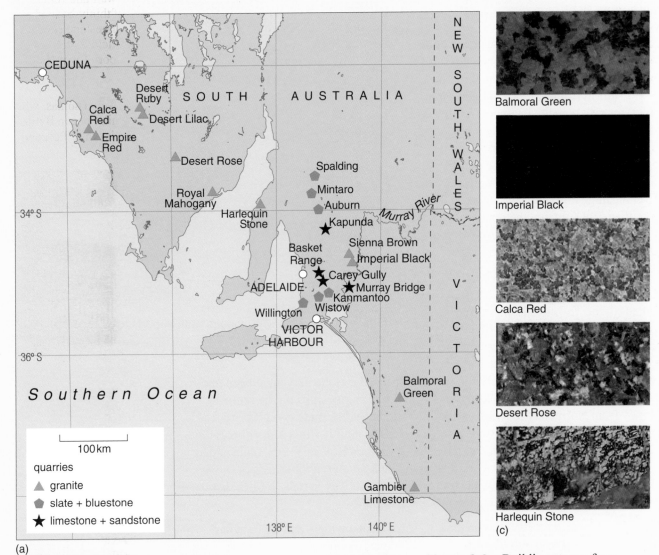

(a)

(c)

(b)

Figure 2.9 Building stones from South Australia. (a) Map of part of South Australia centred on Adelaide, with locations of some historically important and currently operating quarries. (b) Traditional building stones used in Adelaide, South Australia. The walls are of Precambrian siltstone (known as 'bluestone'), picked out in red sandstone and roofed with slate. (c) Selection of images of ornamental stones from South Australia used in marketing.

2.3 Building stones: changing perspectives

2.3.1 From quarry to market

The example of Stonehenge in Box 1.1 illustrates the potential advantages of transporting stone by water, and many civilizations recognized that ships were the ideal, low-cost solution to transporting large quantities of building stone from quarry to market. Thus the Romans shipped granite some 2500 km from Mons Claudianus, in Egypt, for pillars in the Pantheon Temple in Rome. Each column was a single piece of granite almost 12 m high and weighing approximately 60 tonnes. The ease of transporting them by water to Rome clearly offset the huge initial effort of hauling them more than 100 km from the quarry across the desert to the Nile. Figure 2.10 shows routes for transporting stone by sea to various localities in the Roman Empire.

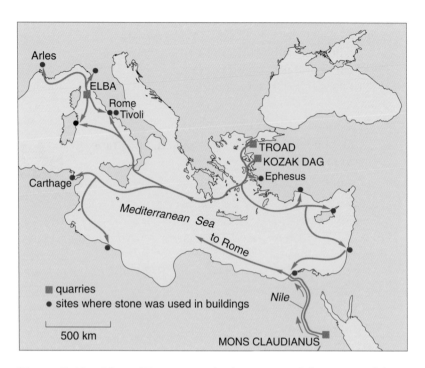

Figure 2.10 Map of Roman granite imports used for ceremonial buildings, 1st to 5th centuries AD.

Many historic British buildings (e.g. Durham Cathedral, the Tower of London, and Windsor Castle) contain Caen limestone from Normandy. This stone was favoured by the Normans because it is an excellent freestone, suited to delicate carving. In some cases, the stone may have been an incidental cargo that was used as **ballast** to stabilize empty ships on the return journey from Normandy to Britain after discharging British trade goods in France. In the modern world, building stone is traded internationally — this is mainly costly ornamental stone that has been cut, polished or carved (Box 2.3). The value added by such processing justifies the cost of shipping bulky material thousands of kilometres, but it is only because the transportation is mostly in bulk, by sea, that the transport costs are low enough to make it economic.

During the Industrial Revolution in the UK, ships traded widely and brought back rock in their holds as ballast, which was dumped near the ports. Places like Newcastle and South Wales, long-standing exporters of coal, accumulated huge piles of ballast, some of which was crushed for use on roads or railway tracks. The term 'ballast' is still used for such crushed rock, even if it comes from a local quarry. Modern bulk vessels use water for ballast.

In Britain, the advent of canals in the latter part of the 18th century, and the introduction of the railways around 1830, made bulk materials more widely available by lowering transport costs. Houses were no longer limited to local materials, resulting in the substitution of many local building materials by those brought in by barge or train. One example is the dramatic increase in the use of roofing slate from North Wales, the Lake District and Cornwall, wherever the railways ran; local materials such as thatch or poor-quality stone were largely

Box 2.3   Shri Swaminarayan Mandir: From India to London

The construction of this Hindu temple in north London (Figure 2.11) in the early 1990s is a striking illustration of how transport and processing costs influence the use of building stone in the modern world. Firstly, the bulk of the stone was sourced from four different countries:

- 2828 tonnes of cream-coloured Bulgarian limestone;
- 2000 tonnes of white marble from Italy (Carrara marble) and India;
- 127 tonnes of Sardinian granite.

The temple was built by a huge team of masons and volunteers from the Hindu community in London. However, before over 26 000 blocks of stone could be pieced together to form the temple, the stone had to be dressed and intricately carved by skilled craftsmen. This work was carried out by over 1500 Indian stonemasons — in India!

- Suggest an economic reason why much of the stone was shipped to India for this processing.

- Savings made by using Indian craftsmen on low wages compared to those in the UK more than offset the cost of shipping the stone out to India and then back to London.

Figure 2.11   Shri Swaminarayan Mandir, Neasden, North London. The exterior walls are a mixture of creamy Bulgarian limestone and white Carrara marble (the stone used by Michelangelo for his famous sculptures), which was also used, along with Indian marble, for carved pillars, steps and internal features. Darker Sardinian granite provides a damp-proof base.

Once each piece had been finished, it was numbered to indicate its place in the finished temple. On arrival in London, the numbered blocks were literally fitted together like a giant jigsaw puzzle.

abandoned. Brick became a cheap substitute for local building stone from the 18th century onwards, contributing to its decline.

The introduction of steel-rimmed carriage wheels demanded harder-wearing cobblestones and kerbstones for Victorian cities. These could now be sourced from granite outcrops as far afield as Cornwall and Scotland — and although the cobbles have mostly disappeared, kerbstones remain in vast numbers, for example the town of Buckingham boasts kerbstones of distinctive Dartmoor granite.

2.3.2   Place value

Because bulk materials such as building stones are relatively low-value commodities, the cost of moving them to where they are needed can soon outstrip their value at the quarry gate (i.e. they have a high place value). This means they tend to be produced in local quarries supplying a relatively small area.

- Would value-added materials, such as granite or marble polished at the quarry site, have a high or low place value?

- They have a *low* place value because they command a *high* price at the quarry gate due to the processing. They can be transported great distances before transport costs significantly affect their price.

Table 2.1   Transport costs for bulk materials in 2004.

Method of transport	Maximum load/t	Cost/£ per tonne km*	Comments
lorry	40	0.1	flexible; small, frequent loads
rail	3 000	0.05	restricted to rail network
barge/small ship	5 000	0.015	canal or coastal sites only
large ship	55 000	0.002	ports with deep water and loading facilities
very large ship	140 000	0.0005	major ports only

* £ per tonne km is the cost of carrying one tonne for one kilometre ($\text{£ t}^{-1} \text{km}^{-1}$).

Question 2.2

(a) From the costs in Table 2.1, how far can a full lorry load of cheap crushed rock be carried by road before the transport cost exceeds the quarry gate cost of £4 per tonne?

(b) How far could the same lorry take a 10-tonne load of cheap roofing slates before the transport cost exceeds their value of £500 per tonne at the quarry gate? (Assume part load costs are the same per km to transport as a full load.)

Transport by road rapidly increases the price of bulk materials with distance from the quarry, whereas rail transport can be less than half the cost per tonne kilometre, especially with well-designed wagons and loading facilities. Transport in the largest ocean carriers, however, can be 100 times cheaper than by rail, which accounts for the international trade in bulk commodities such as coal and cement powder. In the Middle Ages, coal was shipped from Newcastle, England, to London; at the start of the 21st century it was being shipped to London from Newcastle in Australia! In fact, bulk ocean carriers not only allow global trade in physical resources such as coal, oil and iron ore, but also move shipments of waste from one continent to another for disposal. Despite the availability of cheap bulk transport by rail and sea, high transport costs are still a major reason for the decline in the use of natural stone for building in developed countries.

● Why do you think this is so?

○ Not all stone quarries are close to a port, or served by a railway. Most building stones incur road freight costs for the initial journey from quarry to railhead or port, and of course for the last stage of the journey to the construction site if it is inland.

2.3.3   Production of building stones

Through the 20th century, natural stone has been gradually substituted in developed countries by other materials such as brick, clay or cement-based tiles, concrete, steel and glass, particularly in domestic housing. The main reason for this substitution is cost — particularly the cost of dressing natural stone to the required size and shape for building. Bricks and concrete blocks are much easier to make; their production is highly mechanized and, as they are of a standard size and shape, building with them is easier — and cheaper — than with stone.

But how is natural stone worked, and how much does it cost? Table 2.2 compares typical costs for different forms of building stone with those for other building materials.

Table 2.2   Typical early-2000s costs of building materials at the place of extraction.

Material	Working methods	Processing	% waste	On-site value* /£ t^{-1}
thin slabs of cut and polished stone	wedging, cutting, low explosives†	diamond saws and polishing	50–90	250–2500
slate for roofing	wedging, cutting, low explosives†	trimming, hand splitting	80–95	400–1800
building stone, dressed blocks	wedging, cutting, low explosives†	guillotining, trimming, hand dressing	30–50	50–300
stone setts, reclaimed	reclamation		<5	40–120
bricks and tiles from clay	mechanical diggers	grinding, moulding, firing	<3	100–400
cement from limestone and mudstone	mechanical diggers (high explosives‡)	grinding, mixing, firing, grinding	<10	20–50
gypsum	mechanical diggers	grinding, washing	10	5–30
sands and gravels	mechanical diggers	sieving, washing	<10	2–7
crushed rock	high explosives‡	crushing, grading	<10	2–8

* Prices are given in £ per tonne.

† Low explosives 'burn', producing a rapid increase in gas pressure that splits the rock apart with minimal shattering.

‡ High explosives shatter rocks by producing a shock wave that travels through the rock at the speed of sound, so cannot be used for quarrying where dressed or polished stone is being won.

From Table 2.2, you can see that it is the specialized processing that makes building stone so much more expensive than other building materials, whose processing can be mechanized. The most costly commodity in Table 2.2 is polished natural stone, reflecting the skilled labour and specialized machinery involved in processing. Not all this processing is necessarily done at the quarry. Shipping large blocks of stone to countries such as India to be cut, polished and carved (Box 2.3) may make economic sense; if processing and labour costs are relatively low there, the shipping costs will be justified by the stone's added value. This high value also enables visually dramatic polished stone to be exported worldwide and used as a facing on modern buildings. The stone may contribute to the 'corporate identity' of a company — for instance banks generally choose a stone such as granite, suggestive of solidity and dependability. Shopping centres are often lavishly paved and faced with polished stone to create an ambience of luxury and taste. One ubiquitous stone, a dark, crystalline igneous rock – with a characteristic bluish iridescence – from Norway, known as larvikite, can be seen in shopping streets from London to Sydney.

   Is natural stone used more in residential or commercial buildings?

   Commercial buildings use quantities of expensive polished or dressed stone, whereas most domestic houses are constructed mainly of lower-cost concrete blocks and bricks, with fired clay or concrete roof tiles. Natural stone tends to be used only sparingly in modern housing, for instance in polished kitchen worktops.

The high cost of building stones, and their substitution by cheaper materials, has led in some developed nations to the closure of many local dimension stone quarries, leaving only small numbers still operational. Their output is for specialist uses such as buildings in conservation areas where planning requirements demand the use of traditional materials, or the restoration of heritage buildings in the original stone. Recently, there has been a resurgence of demand for natural building stone, prompting old quarries to re-open, particularly in places such as Adelaide, Australia where there is a strong tradition of building in stone. Meanwhile, major producers of popular ornamental stones such as Carrara marble have increased their output — in fact overall production in the European Union increased almost threefold between 1986 and 2000.

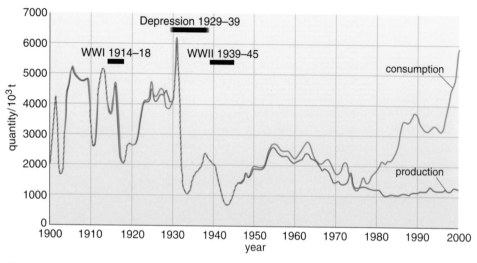

Figure 2.12 Graph of consumption (red) and production (blue) of dimension stone in the USA during the 20th century.

Question 2.3

Using the information in Figure 2.12:

(a) Compare the effects of each of the two World Wars and the Depression of the early 1930s on the production of dimension stone in the USA.

(b) Compare the trends in production and consumption of building stone in the USA from 1950 to 2000.

(c) The production and consumption graphs *diverge* in the USA after about 1980. What does this indicate?

2.3.4 Environmental impact of building stone quarries

Small quarries with low output, characteristic of building stone extraction in the UK at the start of the 21st century, tend to be fairly 'environmentally friendly' (Figure 2.13). High explosives — which would shatter the stone — are avoided; heavy machinery is employed sparingly; and associated traffic is light due to the low output of small quarries. However, large dimension stone quarries do exist, notably in countries where competition for land use is less intense than in the UK, such as India, Australia, and even Italy. Quarries that produce crushed rock for aggregate are generally much larger than those for dimension stone, with a greater environmental impact.

In the UK, quarries are commonly sited in scenic areas, so even extending them is subject to planning restrictions. Underground mining provides a solution to many surface environmental problems, with an extra 'out of sight, out of mind' perspective, but is still relatively uncommon — even in the UK where land is at a premium. However, limestone has been mined underground in Bath, England, and widely in the USA, though most subterranean stone mines in the USA produce crushed rock rather than dimension stone. It is likely, however, that restrictions on surface quarrying will increasingly drive the extraction of stone underground.

Figure 2.13   A small UK quarry in Gloucestershire that produces sandstone for paving, walling and garden features, as well as for the restoration of historic buildings.

2.4   Legacies of building stone extraction

2.4.1   Abandoned quarries

The majority of building stones have traditionally been worked in open pits, which are easy to abandon and easy to re-open. The late 20th century saw more serious consideration of the role of disused quarries in the environment, with the realization that a large hole in the ground may in fact be an asset or an opportunity, rather than a problem. Old quarries can become nature reserves, industrial museums, recreational lakes, or even waste-disposal sites. Any modern industrialized society produces huge volumes of waste, including domestic refuse. So filling large quarries with waste and adding a landscaped veneer of topsoil might seem an ideal solution. However, there is a significant risk of contamination from the waste unless the quarries are made watertight before tipping.

● What underground resource is most threatened by pollution from landfill?

○ Groundwater. If contaminants can percolate from the waste through the quarry floor, they may pollute water supplies.

Surface water can percolate through quarried strata that are porous and permeable (e.g. sandstones) into permeable strata at depth known as **aquifers**, from which water may be pumped for human consumption. The percolation can be so slow that it may be years before pollution is detected, by which time a huge 'plume' of contamination may have entered the aquifer (Figure 2.14). It may be years before the pollutants disperse, even after pollution is stopped at source. These risks, and the small size of many building stone quarries, means that

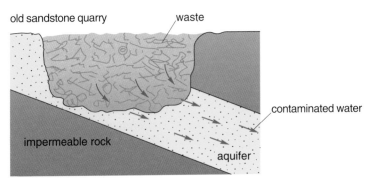

Figure 2.14   Contamination of an underground aquifer by waste dumped in an old quarry in porous, permeable sandstone.

other sites such as large brick clay pits are used for waste disposal instead (Chapter 3). Other uses are therefore favoured for old stone quarries. Many are cleaned up and, once the vegetation has regenerated, become nature reserves, often showcasing the exposed geology. Limestone quarries in the UK are very valuable as they mimic the conditions of rare limestone pavement habitats and develop a distinctive lime-loving flora, including orchids. Bowlees Country Park in Teesdale, Yorkshire, is one example. Some quarries with strong regional associations are used as sites for museums or visitor centres, such as the National Stone Centre located in old Carboniferous limestone quarries at Wirksworth in Derbyshire, or the Slate Caverns at Blaenau Ffestiniog, North Wales.

(a)

2.4.2 Old subsurface mines

If a particular building stone was especially prized, surface pits may have been extended underground in the form of shallow mines. Bath stone was mined in this way at Bath in Somerset. It has been calculated that between 1720 and 1850 approximately 750 000 m^3 of excellent building stone (oolite) was extracted. The stone was mined in a series of chambers, or 'rooms', separated by supporting pillars (Figure 2.15a). As the roof was 4–8 m thick at that time, with no houses above, the risk of subsidence or collapse was hardly an issue.

With time, however, thinning of the pillars occurred where pieces of rock flaked off along fractures and joints in the limestone — or where stone was 'robbed' after the mines were closed. Similar spalling of rock from the ceiling has also thinned the overlying roof. Both processes have probably been exacerbated by increasing traffic vibration. The overall effect is that, in places, the mine roof has thinned to within 2–3 m of the surface. Houses have also been built on top of the mine (Figure 2.15b). By the early 1990s, there was a very real danger of subsidence or collapse. In 1993, contrasting proposals were put forward to address the problem. Two schemes suggested filling the mines, but with different materials: one with concrete incorporating crushed Bath stone waste from nearby workings, and the other with a mixture of cement and pulverized fuel ash (PFA, an inert waste product of coal-fired power stations). Both were high-cost strategies (between £20 million and £50 million). Vigorous opposition cited the value of the mines as a haven for greater and lesser horseshoe bats, as well as questioning the inertness of PFA in the long term. Local groups also wanted to preserve parts of the mines as important archaeological features. By the year 2000, the use of PFA as an infill material had been rejected, and a further review was under way.

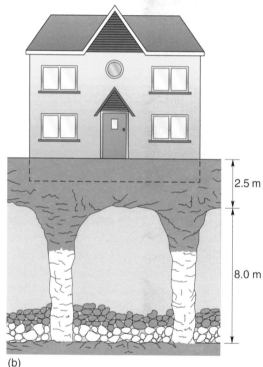
(b)

Figure 2.15 Bath stone mines.
(a) Part of the mine in the Combe Down area, with pillars separating 'rooms' from which the oolite was extracted. (b) Deterioration of the underground Bath mines due to roof spalling and thinning of the pillars. The white pillar sections indicate the extent of the oolite bed for which the mine was worked.

Just as with quarries, some old underground stone mines present opportunities rather than problems. Old mines in the Permian sandstone beneath Nottingham, UK have been used as cellars, while limestone mines in the United States, for example, have a variety of uses — such as archive storage, warehouse storage and commercial enterprise. On a grander scale, old limestone mines under Kansas City, Missouri have been converted into an entire commercial district known as Subtropolis, which provides storage and office space located 50 m below ground level (Figure 2.16). Advantages include a controlled environment, security, low rent and running costs, stability and low fire risk. Temperature is relatively constant (~ 18 °C), favouring specialized applications such as computer labs, and food or film storage — the original reels of 'Gone with the Wind' and 'Ben Hur' are now stored in Subtropolis.

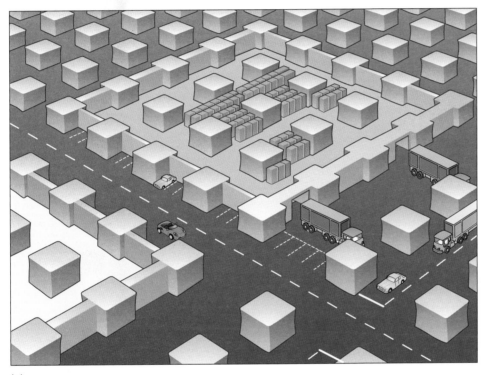

(a)

(b)

Figure 2.16   (a) Schematic diagram of part of Subtropolis, Kansas City, Missouri. (b) At work in Subtropolis.

2.5   Summary of Chapter 2

1   Natural stone is extracted directly from the bedrock, unlike many modern building materials that are either derived from drift, or require extensive processing. For durability, either crystalline (igneous or metamorphic) rock, or well-lithified sedimentary rock, is used.

2   Older rocks tend to be more lithified, and thus stronger and more durable, as compaction and cementation processes decrease their porosity. In the UK, building stones are scarce in the southeast, reflecting the relative youth of the sedimentary rocks located there. The north and west of Britain, by contrast, are underlain by rocks more suitable for building: a mixture of older sediments, igneous, and metamorphic rocks.

3   Most building stone has traditionally been extracted close to the building site, resulting in distinctive vernacular architecture in many areas. Valued stones, such as freestones, could be transported great distances, especially by sea. This practice continues into the 21st century, with vast bulk carriers shipping stone around the world.

4   The influence of cost, and the crucial contribution that transport makes to the costs of building materials, is fundamental to the concept of place value. The lower the cost of a material at the quarry gate, the higher its place value: it is uneconomic to transport it far.

5   Processing costs, related mainly to wage levels and energy costs, increase the value of natural stone significantly, lowering its place value. Thus in industrialized nations, the uses of natural stone are mainly limited to ornamental facing slabs and restoration projects. Cheaper, modern materials such as concrete and brick have substituted for stone in these countries.

6   The environmental impact of opening or extending a quarry has become a serious issue for the extraction industry in recent decades. Abandoned quarries and subsurface mines may pose problems of groundwater contamination from poorly designed landfill, or of subsidence. Opportunities to restore and exploit old quarries exist, while underground mines may have a variety of applications.

CLAYS FOR BRICKS AND BEYOND

3

3.1 Clays and clay minerals

What do we mean by 'clay'? The term is used for:

- 'heavy' soils that become waterlogged in winter but bake hard and crack up in dry periods;
- fine-grained, soft rocks that can be moulded when wet;
- the finest sedimentary particles (less than 0.002 mm in size);
- layered aluminosilicate minerals formed by weathering.

It is the presence of clay minerals that is common to all of the above definitions. If you shake up some soil with water and then let it settle for a few minutes, the finest material, still in suspension and making the water cloudy, will be chiefly small flakes of clay minerals (Figure 3.1). Clay rocks (also known as mudrocks or mudstones) contain a high proportion of clay minerals, as do clay soils, while the majority of fine sedimentary particles are also clay minerals. Ancient civilizations had an intuitive grasp of the nature of clay — it is easily moulded when wet, but bakes hard once dried in the sun (or fired). It was the ideal material for pottery, bricks, and religious artefacts.

Figure 3.1 Clay mineral grains are too small to be seen under even the highest-power optical microscope. This SEM image shows typical six-sided, flat, flake-like crystals of the clay mineral kaolinite.

There is a spectrum of clay-bearing sediments that runs from clay-rich soils, through drift deposits laid down by retreating ice sheets, to older lithified rocks such as mudstones or shales. These all contain mineral impurities such as iron oxides or quartz, and organic matter. With increasing depths of burial, pore water in a mudrock is gradually expelled by compaction and heating, while organic matter may be converted to oil or gas. Mudrocks are transformed to slate or schist with further burial or compression.

3.1.1 The origin of clays

Most clay minerals are the products of subaerial weathering, yet the bulk of clay rocks in the geological record were deposited in seas and oceans.

- Why are many clays deposited so far from their site of formation?

- Clay minerals tend to form minute particles that can be transported very easily, and very far, in water. A muddy-looking river carries large amounts of clay particles in suspension that will only settle out when the river reaches a quieter environment such as a lake, an estuary or the sea.

Another property that allows clay particles to travel long distances is that they tend to carry a small negative charge on their surface. As like charges repel, the aggregation of clay mineral particles to larger clots, which would sink more rapidly, is inhibited in fresh water. Materials that behave in this way are known as **colloids**, and are held in colloidal solution. Colloidal particles have diameters in the range 10^{-9}–10^{-6} m, effectively in a state somewhere between ions in solution and 'true' particles (ones that can be filtered out) in suspension. When they reach the sea, however, there is a much higher concentration of dissolved positive ions, such as Na^+, Mg^{2+}, K^+, Ca^{2+}, which neutralize the negative charges on the clay mineral surface, and so enable the particles to stick together, a process called **flocculation**. These larger particles then fall to the sea floor to form a layer of sediment. Clays that have been transported and then laid down as sediments are called sedimentary clays; these are usually composed not of a single clay mineral, such as kaolinite, but of a mixture of clay minerals from a variety of sources.

Clay deposits, just like sands and gravels, are also subject to the *physical* processes of erosion, transport and deposition, which tend to differentiate particles on the basis of their physical properties such as size and density. Understanding these processes is important for commodities like aggregates, where grain size is crucial to their exploitation. However, clay minerals are formed by *chemical* breakdown of silicate minerals at or near the Earth's surface, and in some cases this chemical control produces deposits of a specific clay type, that may be useful for industrial applications that demand high purity. Clay deposits found where they originally formed are known as **residual clay** deposits. A prime example in the UK is the china clay (largely kaolinite) of Cornwall, which is worked from the 'pockets' where it formed by a combination of low-temperature alteration of underlying granite by acidic hydrothermal fluids generated as the granite cooled (at ~ 270 Ma), and relatively recent weathering. So what happens when granite suffers weathering in a wet temperate climate like that in the UK (Figure 3.2)?

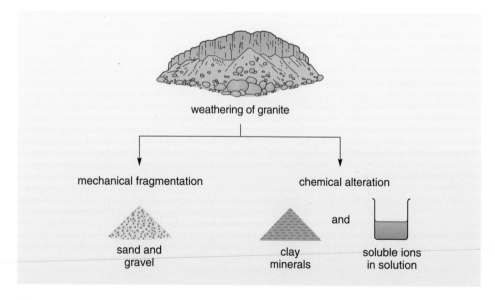

Figure 3.2 The weathering of granite. Physical weathering (such as frost action) splits the rock into fragments. Chemical weathering attacks the feldspars and micas to form clay minerals. Chemically and physically resistant grains such as quartz are carried away to form sand and gravel deposits. Very soluble ions (Na^+, Mg^{2+}, K^+ and Ca^{2+}) are carried away in solution.

The main chemical weathering agent is rainwater, which is mildly acidic even in unpolluted areas because it dissolves carbon dioxide. This reacts with the water to form bicarbonate ions and hydrogen ions, whose concentration determines the acidity of the solution:

$$\underset{\substack{\text{carbon} \\ \text{dioxide}}}{CO_2} + \underset{\text{water}}{H_2O} = \underset{\substack{\text{hydrogen} \\ \text{ions}}}{H^+} + \underset{\substack{\text{bicarbonate} \\ \text{ions}}}{HCO_3^-} \qquad (3.1)$$

The three main minerals in granite — quartz, feldspar and mica — respond differently to chemical weathering processes. Quartz is resistant to chemical attack, and so will be carried away as mineral grains, along with larger rock fragments, to form sands and gravels along the river valleys. Feldspars and micas, however, are chemically attacked by the rainwater, which carries away elements like sodium, potassium and calcium in solution as ions (Na^+, K^+ and Ca^{2+}). The clay minerals left behind contain most of the original aluminium and silicon from the feldspars and micas: the more soluble ions (Na^+, K^+ and Ca^{2+}) end up in the oceans. A simple clay-forming reaction is the chemical breakdown of potassium feldspar during weathering to form kaolinite:

$$\underset{\substack{\text{potassium} \\ \text{feldspar}}}{2KAlSi_3O_8} + \underset{\text{acidic rainwater}}{2H^+ + H_2O} = \underset{\text{kaolinite}}{Al_2Si_2O_5(OH)_4} + \underset{\substack{\text{ions and silica} \\ \text{removed in solution}}}{2K^+ + 4SiO_2} \qquad (3.2)$$

Water combines with aluminium and some silica from the original feldspar to form kaolinite, while the potassium and the rest of the silica are carried away in solution, along with the bicarbonate ions from the dissolved carbon dioxide. Potassium feldspar is a major constituent of granite. As the feldspar decomposes, a tough granite will eventually crumble into a mixture of quartz crystals (sand) and a soft mass of the new clay mineral, kaolinite. A dramatic example of this process can be seen in wet tropical climates such as Brazil where, in a road cutting through hard granite, little fresh rock will be visible within 10–20 years; in the cooler temperatures of the UK, however, weathering reactions occur at a much slower rate.

●   Does Equation 3.2 suggest that rainwater is the only solution that could break feldspar down to kaolinite?

○   No — the hydrogen ions and water could come from any acidic solution.

In fact, acids within soil (produced by plants and animals) are probably more important than those in rainwater. However, in industrial areas, sulphur dioxide produced by the burning of sulphur-rich fuels, and nitrogen oxides from car exhausts, both increase the acidity of rainwater (producing 'acid rain').

Clay minerals usually belong to one of three main groups, **kaolinite**, **illite** and **smectite**, reflecting the type of mineral that broke down to form them:

● feldspars break down to kaolinite, as you have seen;

● micas generally weather to give illite, which retains some potassium in its crystal lattice;

● ferromagnesian igneous minerals, such as pyroxenes and amphiboles, weather to yield the clay mineral smectite, which contains sodium, calcium and some water *between* the layers, as well as iron and magnesium *within* the layers.

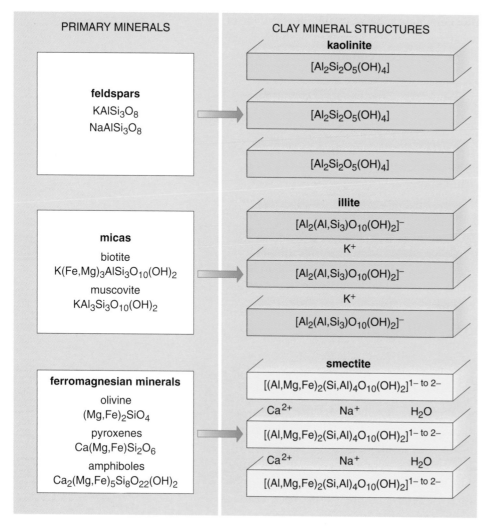

Figure 3.3 Derivation, composition and structure of clay minerals. The relationship between the major groups of original minerals (left) and the composition and structure of the clay minerals that each forms on weathering (right). The sketches of clay mineral structures show how the negative charges on the aluminosilicate layers of illite and smectite are balanced by the positive charges on metal ions.

Figure 3.3 shows the layered chemical structure of the different clay mineral groups.

In many cases, the original clay minerals change their chemical composition when buried and heated deep in the Earth. The main effect of these changes over time is to increase the amount of illite at the expense of smectite, and to a lesser extent of kaolinite, so that older clays tend to be richer in illite.

The ions *between* the aluminosilicate layers in clay minerals (Figure 3.3) balance the ionic charges *on* the layers:

- *kaolinite*: the aluminosilicate layers are electrically neutral; no ions are present between the layers.

- *illite*: the aluminosilicate layers are negatively charged; overall neutrality is achieved by the presence of potassium ions, K^+, between the layers.

- *smectite*: the aluminosilicate layers are more strongly negatively charged; neutrality is achieved by the presence of calcium and sodium ions between the layers. Note that water molecules are also present.

⬤ What is the most obvious chemical distinction between the three groups of clay minerals?

◯ Whether or not the clays contain ions between the layers, and what those ions are.

The presence of positively charged metal ions between the negatively charged layers in illite and smectite leads to strong ionic bonding between the layers. The absence of these charged interlayer ions in kaolinite means that its layers are only weakly bonded together, and so it is relatively soft.

The chemistry of clays has implications for their applications. Their major use, brick-making, relies on their composition for the chemical changes that occur on firing. Before examining that process, however, we will look at a group of clays whose chemistry has fostered a surprising variety of uses.

3.1.2 Smectite clays — mineralogical machines

These clays are formed naturally by alteration of volcanic ashes deposited in seas or lakes, though increasingly they are modified, or actually synthesized, in a range of compositions. Most are earthy brown or green in colour, but rare white bentonite clays form from the alteration of volcanic rocks rich in quartz and feldspar by hydrothermal fluids. The world's largest producers of smectite clays are the USA and Greece, though deposits are found worldwide.

A feature of the complex representative formula of smectite (Figure 3.3) is the presence of cations and water molecules between the aluminosilicate layers in their structure. By exchanging these cations with different ions from other substances, the clays are transformed chemically and physically. They act as 'mineralogical machines', able to expand, form gels, absorb, and swap ions with chemical solutions.

The three main types of smectite are distinguished on the basis of their interlayer cations:

- bentonite (Na smectite);
- fuller's earth (Ca smectite);
- hectorite (Mg–Li smectite).

Bentonite is the most widely used smectite clay — though not the most naturally abundant. Incredibly, it can absorb *up to 15 times its own weight of water* — but an even more remarkable property is displayed when a slurry of bentonite in water is stirred energetically. The water enters between the clay platelets, prising them apart (Figure 3.4a) to form a low-viscosity liquid (Figure 3.4b). If left to rest, the platelets reorganize themselves into a structure dictated by the attraction and repulsion of charge on the clay surfaces, thickening the slurry to form a gel (Figure 3.4c).

Figure 3.4 shows that each clay platelet has positively charged edges, but negatively charged flat surfaces. Because each edge is attracted to a face, and vice-versa, a loose framework (rather like a 'house of cards') forms, within which large volumes of water are 'trapped' (Figure 3.4c). Shaking or stirring disturbs the framework, returning the gel back to liquid (Figure 3.4b), but if left to stand it will once more transform into a gel.

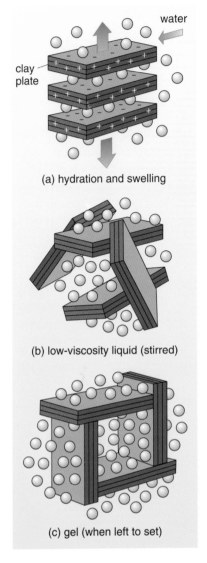

(a) hydration and swelling

(b) low-viscosity liquid (stirred)

(c) gel (when left to set)

Figure 3.4 Three stages in the formation of a gel when water is added to bentonite clay. (a) Water molecules (blue circles) absorbed between the aluminosilicate layers cause the clay to swell. (b) As more water is added, the clay platelets disperse into the liquid and can move freely if stirred. (c) Once stirring ceases, the electrostatic forces between charged surfaces on the clay platelets take effect, reorganizing the platelets into a loose structure that traps water, forming a gel. Note: negatively charged surfaces are green; positively charged surfaces are brown.

This property, known as **thixotropy**, is probably most familiar as the principle behind non-drip paints, and many such paints contain bentonite. Clays can also affect the consistency of other products more subtly, and this leads to their inclusion in many paints, cosmetics and detergents. Thixotropy is also the basis for one of the most important uses of bentonites: in drilling oil wells. During drilling, a clay slurry ('mud') is pumped into the borehole. While the drill is rotating, the clay remains a fluid acting as a lubricant, but when the drill rods are withdrawn from the hole the clay sets to a gel. This property is particularly useful for supporting borehole walls if drilling in unconsolidated sediments. Dense minerals, such as barite, are commonly mixed with the mud to raise its density and prevent a 'blow-out' if the hole intersects an oil or gas reservoir — crucial to the safety of a drill rig and its crew.

- What physical property (apart from thixotropy) might favour the use of bentonite over other clays as a supporting medium for these heavy minerals?

- Its density: bentonite is denser than other common clays. This is due to the iron and magnesium it contains, resulting from its origin as a weathering product of ferromagnesian minerals such as pyroxene.

Bentonites are very plastic clays, ideal for forming an impermeable lining for the floor and walls of old quarries being prepared for waste disposal (see Section 3.5), and as other types of environmental barrier to stop contamination of groundwater. Figure 3.5 summarizes the main uses of bentonite clays.

Treating Ca smectites with strong acids increases their surface area, making them more reactive. As the surface of the clay particles provides an ideal substrate for chemical reactions, these 'activated earths' have a wide range of applications, including bleaching and catalysis (Figure 3.6). Both bentonite and Ca smectite are used as 'fining' agents for clarifying wines and beers. The clay particles attract the fine, suspended sediment that causes cloudiness in these drinks, helping it to settle out, as well as removing some of the colouring compounds to leave the desired clear beverage. Honey, sugar and many cooking oils are also treated in this way.

The name 'fuller's earth' refers to the traditional use of Ca smectite clays for cleaning ('fulling')

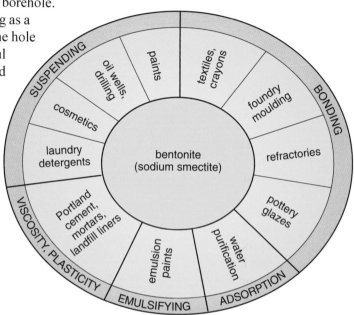

Figure 3.5 Some uses of bentonite discussed in the text, together with a selection of other applications to illustrate the wide range of uses for these clays.

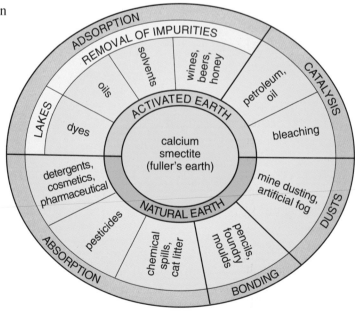

Figure 3.6 Some uses of calcium smectites discussed in the text, together with a selection of other applications to illustrate the wide range of uses for these clays.

wool. This exploited their strong absorbency, particularly for oil and grease; they are also used to clean up after chemical or waste spills. Fuller's earth is also used in smaller spills — for cat litter — as it not only absorbs but helps deodorize!

Fuller's earth is frequently mixed with sodium carbonate to make synthetic bentonite. The exchange of sodium ions for calcium ions in the clay produces a Na smectite which has many of the properties of its natural counterpart.

- Why is it preferable to process Ca smectite than simply to mine fresh bentonite?

- Natural deposits containing Ca smectite are more abundant than bentonite, so it can be more economic to process abundant fuller's earth for bentonite.

Around 12 Mt of smectite clay are extracted annually worldwide, around 30% of which is from the USA, with other important producers being Greece, Germany, Italy, Turkey, Japan and India. The UK produced around 44 000 t in 2002 from deposits in southern England, at Woburn, Redhill and Baulking. Extraction is generally in open pits (Figure 3.7).

Figure 3.7 View of bentonite quarry on the Greek island of Milos, showing opencast extraction using benches. Extensive deposits of bentonite were formed when volcanic rocks were leached by acidic hydrothermal fluids.

Box 3.1   Hectorite — up close and personal

This high-value, light coloured, magnesium–lithium smectite clay is worked only in California, USA, where volcanic ash accumulated in shallow lakes associated with evaporite deposits. An unusual interaction of the volcanic tuffs with active hot springs, which brought Li and Mg up from depth, altered the tuffs to produce this rare Li–Mg smectite.

Hectorite is prized for its effects on the viscosity of other materials: it makes paints flow more easily, cosmetics apply more smoothly, and ink transfer to paper more efficiently. Look at the ingredients list on a can of deodorant. Many include hectorite, which allows the contents through the spray nozzle as a low-viscosity liquid that then solidifies on the body. Many lipsticks also rely on hectorite to form a solid in the stick, but liquefy under pressure when applied to the lips for ease of spreading. It then forms a durable, plastic, glossy coating. Of course pressure applied to the lips will cause the material to liquefy again, capable of leaving a tell-tale mark…

Rare natural hectorite cost around $2000 per tonne in the early 21st century. This high price has encouraged several companies to manufacture and market synthetic hectorite substitutes. These artificial magnesium smectites have a range of Li contents, and highly specified properties tailored to the needs of the main consuming industries (e.g. cosmetics, paint, ceramics, and printing inks); they command a similar price to natural hectorite.

3.2 Clays and brick-making

3.2.1 Distribution and variety of UK brick clays

In the British Isles, most pre-Carboniferous mudstones (see Figure 2.6) have been deformed and metamorphosed to slates or schists, unsuitable for making bricks, so it is generally the younger, sedimentary mudstones that are used for this purpose.

Question 3.1

(a) With reference to Figure 2.6, which parts of the UK are *unlikely* to have abundant deposits of brick clay in the bedrock (i.e. not as superficial deposits)?

(b) What does this distribution imply about the distance between the majority of UK brick clay deposits and their potential markets?

You can check your answers to Question 3.1 on Figure 3.8, which shows the distribution of important UK brick clays; more information on these clays is given in Table 3.1.

The three main sources of sedimentary clay for the brick and tile industry are:

- Carboniferous mudstones, used for bricks especially in the UK coalfields, i.e. close to their extraction sites;

- the Jurassic Oxford Clay, traditionally used for supplying bricks to much of southern England;

- a variety of smaller superficial deposits of Pleistocene and Recent age occurring locally throughout lowland Britain.

Table 3.1   Most important brick clay-bearing strata of Britain.

Local name of clay	Geological age	Age of rock/Ma	% of UK clay output*	Environment	Main clay minerals
alluvium, glacial clay	Recent Pleistocene	0.012	13	rivers, ice	various
ball clay, London Clay	Tertiary	38.55	2	rivers	kaolinite
Gault Clay, Weald Clay	Cretaceous	135	13	marine and estuaries	illite and smectite
Kimmeridge, Oxford and Lias Clays	Jurassic	180	16	marine and estuaries	illite and kaolinite
Mercia Mudstone†	Triassic	225	16	desert lakes	illite
Etruria Marl	Carboniferous	290	5	lakes	illite
Coal Measures	Carboniferous	345	34	swamps, deltas	illite, kaolinite

* approximately 1% of UK output is from older mudstones.
† The Mercia Mudstone Group was formerly known as the Keuper Marl.

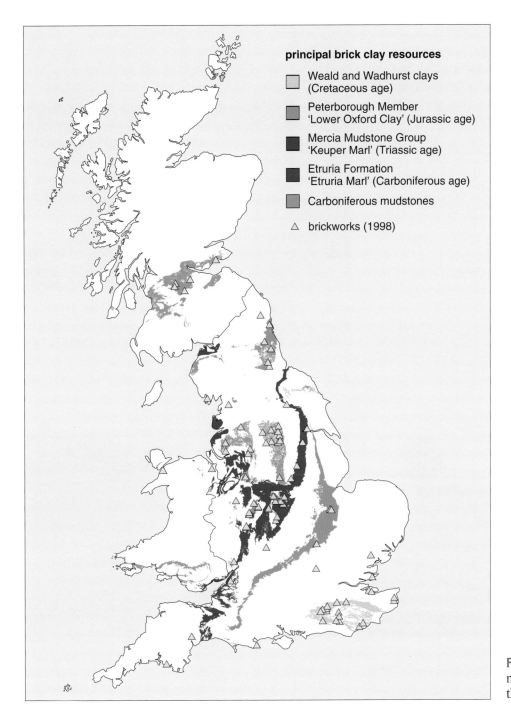

principal brick clay resources

☐ Weald and Wadhurst clays (Cretaceous age)

☐ Peterborough Member 'Lower Oxford Clay' (Jurassic age)

☐ Mercia Mudstone Group 'Keuper Marl' (Triassic age)

☐ Etruria Formation 'Etruria Marl' (Carboniferous age)

☐ Carboniferous mudstones

△ brickworks (1998)

Figure 3.8 Outcrops of the main brick-making clays in the UK.

⬤ Why might superficial clays formed during the last glacial period be less satisfactory than Jurassic clays as the basis for a large-scale brick-making industry?

⬤ Large-scale extraction for brick-making will favour thick, extensive strata of clays such as the Oxford Clay, rather than scattered, thin and variable superficial deposits such as the glacial clays.

3.2.2 The brick-making process

For centuries, early civilizations in the Near East and Mesopotamia used sun-dried clay as bricks, and they are still widely used in arid countries — the mosque at Djenne, Mali, is an impressive, modern, mud-brick building (Figure 3.9). However, since at least 5000 BC, clay has been fired to high temperatures, causing a kind of 'artificial metamorphism' that makes a stronger, more water-resistant brick suitable for a wide range of climates. Modern brick-making begins with the extraction of clay from large pits (Figure 3.10), and it is then ground and mixed with water so it can be extruded or pressed into moulds, forming so-called 'green' bricks. Slow drying of these bricks releases most of the water before firing in a kiln.

At firing temperatures of 1000–1200 °C, clay minerals break down as water is expelled from their structure to form new **anhydrous** minerals (literally minerals 'without water') in a dehydration reaction.

Figure 3.9   Djenne Mosque, Mali, Africa, which was rebuilt in 1907 on the site of an earlier mosque that dated back to the 13th century. Mud bricks are unsuitable for wetter climates but are reasonably durable in arid conditions.

Figure 3.10   Brickworks in Turkey (a and b) during the 1970s and the UK (c) during the 1990s. (a) Clay is ground and mixed in a horse-drawn pug mill. (b) Bricks are hand-shaped and laid out to air-dry. The dried bricks are stacked in a clamp kiln for firing (background). (c) Aerial view of Stewartby brickworks, UK. Chimney stacks rise above the kilns; flooded pits are on the left.

For example, kaolinite breaks down to an aluminosilicate mineral, mullite, and quartz, by this dehydration reaction:

$$3Al_2Si_2O_5(OH)_4 \ = \ Al_6Si_2O_{13} \ + \ 4SiO_2 \ + \ 6H_2O \tag{3.3}$$
$$\text{kaolinite} \qquad \text{mullite} \quad \text{quartz} \quad \text{water}$$

After firing, the brick contains an interlocking network of long, thin, mullite crystals (Figure 3.11), quartz and some glass, which make the brick hard and strong. (Compare Figure 3.11 with Figure 3.1 to assess the change in microscopic structure that provides this strength.)

● Are the clay in Figure 3.1 and the brick in Figure 3.11 porous materials?

○ Yes, both materials contain microscopic pore spaces that could absorb water.

Although porous, most clays are impermeable because the platy clay mineral grains tend to align themselves when compressed, leaving no easy pathway for fluid flow. This is the main reason that land underlain by clay is often poorly drained, with bodies of standing water.

Have you ever thought why dark-grey or muddy-brown wet clay changes to bright red bricks, tiles or clay pipes on firing? The reason is that virtually all natural mudstones contain iron oxides and hydroxides, and iron can exist in two different states. In the iron(II) state (the reduced or ferrous state), it forms mainly dark-grey compounds, which give the dark colours to many sediments. Firing in air causes **oxidation** of the iron compounds in the clay to form the red–brown iron oxide, haematite, where the iron is in the iron(III) state (the oxidized or ferric state). Similarly, sandstones such as the Penrith sandstone (Figure 2.7a) owe their distinctive red colour to haematite formed by oxidation of iron-bearing minerals in a hot desert. Sometimes if you break a bright red brick you find a dark-grey centre inside; this is because during firing the outside of the brick recrystallized and sealed out the oxygen before all the iron compounds in the centre had been oxidized. Lastly, brick colour also varies with iron content: 8–10% iron produces the familiar red bricks, but lower proportions (~ 3% iron) give a white or cream colour. Grey and brown colours can be achieved by adding small amounts (1–4%) of manganese dioxide, while yellow bricks are made from a mixture of clay and chalk.

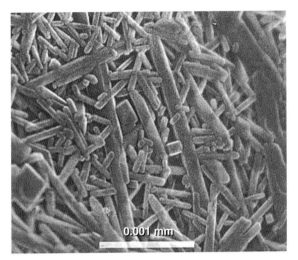

Figure 3.11   Needle-shaped crystals of mullite, which are formed by heating kaolinite to high temperatures during brick-making.

There are many other minor metal constituents in naturally occurring clay, such as Mg^{2+}, Ca^{2+}, Na^+ and K^+, and these tend to act as '**fluxes**' during firing; that is, they promote melting by forming silicate liquids. These liquids cool to form a glassy coat on the new mineral particles. This binds the brick together and reduces its porosity. The amount of liquid has to be kept very small during firing so that the bricks do not 'sag' and come out of the kiln in irregular shapes, or — in the extreme case — fuse together. The dark-grey–blue 'engineering' bricks used in structures such as railway bridges are produced by firing to a higher temperature where rather more melting of the clay under reducing conditions occurs (hence the colour). This produces a much stronger brick for 'demanding' load-bearing structures.

○ What other important properties of engineering bricks are a result of
   considerable melting in their formation?

○ As their pores have been sealed by the silicate glass, these bricks are
   quite impermeable, and have minimal porosity.

Old bricks fired at low temperatures could be quite porous and permeable,
allowing damp to penetrate through walls. A drop of water put onto the surface
of a permeable brick will be absorbed, but with impermeable engineering
bricks, water always stays on the surface, which is characteristically smooth
and glossy. Their impermeability meant that engineering bricks were often
used for the 'damp-proof' course in 19th-century houses.

There are also non-metallic elements present in most natural clays, such as
sulphur (S), chlorine (Cl) and fluorine (F). During firing, these elements may
be driven off as volatile compounds, together with the water. Often, the
effects of these emissions can be seen near kilns where clay is fired — for
example, the etching of glass windows by fluorine compounds. There has been
much concern that some of the emissions from brickworks have been
responsible for fluorine-related diseases in cattle in surrounding areas.

3.3   Brick production and use through time

3.3.1   Past trends in production and use

The Romans used fired bricks extensively for building, including triangular
bricks in the Colosseum, although most Roman bricks were broad and flat,
rather like modern floor tiles. It was the Romans who introduced bricks to
Britain, but the skill of brick-making was lost until its re-introduction from
Flanders in the 13th century. Many buildings before then re-used Roman bricks
from ruined villas — an example of the recycling of building materials that was
probably common, but less obvious, with local stone. Colchester Castle,
finished in 1080, used Roman bricks that were almost a millennium old. When
timber-built London was largely destroyed in the Great Fire of 1666, bricks
became the favoured material for rebuilding, and during the Industrial
Revolution they became the dominant building material in the burgeoning cities.
This pattern of substitution was echoed in new colonies such as New South
Wales, where early timber structures were rapidly replaced with brick
buildings; Government House, the first brick building, was completed just
16 months after the colonists' first landfall in Australia. A small number of
bricks (5000) were even shipped out in the First Fleet to the colony. Bricks
were ubiquitous in Victorian houses, warehouses, factories, mill chimneys, and
railway structures (embankment walls and viaducts; Figure 3.12). Handmade,
fired clay tiles were used for roofing prior to Victorian times. They were
widely substituted by slates brought in from western Britain on the railways, or
machine-made clay tiles during Victorian times.

The second half of the 20th century has seen bricks displaced by concrete as
the main structural building material, as railways have been superseded by
motorways and airport runways. Large, modern buildings tend to use a steel or
concrete load-bearing frame on concrete foundations, with walls of glass,

Figure 3.12 Stockport viaduct (550 m long, 32 m high, 27 arches), one of the largest brick structures in the world. It was first built in 21 months during 1839–40, using 11 million bricks and nearly one-third of a million tonnes of sandstone slabs, and carried the Manchester to Crewe railway line over the Mersey gap. The whole structure was doubled in size in 1887–89 by building an identical structure alongside, to widen the line to four tracks.

concrete, or light, cement-based blocks. Such blocks are cheaper to produce and, due to their low density, can be made six times the volume of a brick, making any wall quicker and thus cheaper to build from blocks. Their low density is partly due to their high porosity, which provides better thermal insulation than clay bricks, allowing them to meet the higher insulation standards specified for all modern buildings. Just as with natural stone, bricks tend to be confined to the decorative and durable outer 'skin' of walls in modern houses (these are known as 'facing' bricks (Figure 3.13)).

- What materials have replaced clay-based roof tiles and natural slate from Victorian times in Britain?

- Predominately cement-based tiles, but also concrete (flat roofs), glass, plastic-based tiles, metal (corrugated iron), **asbestos**-reinforced sheets, and even solar panels.

At the other extreme, below ground a similar range of materials has largely replaced earthenware pipes or brick-lined sewers: large-diameter pipes are made of concrete or cast iron, with smaller pipes being made of plastic. Earthenware pipes are retained for aggressive effluents such as sewage that could corrode less-resistant materials.

Question 3.2

(a) From the preceding discussion, deduce the overall trend in demand for bricks in the UK during the second half of the 20th century.

(b) To what extent do you think the substitution of bricks by cement-based blocks was based on *economic* and/or *technological* factors?

Figure 3.13 Section through a wall under construction in a modern house. Low-density, cement-based blocks (grey) and an outer skin of smaller clay facing bricks (red) enclose a cavity part-filled with fibreglass insulation.

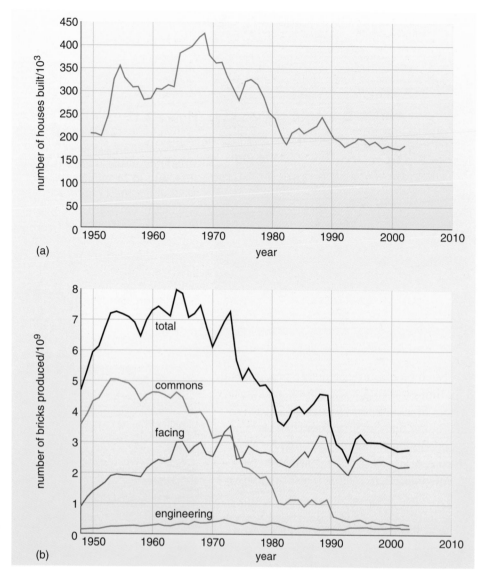

Figure 3.14 (a) Numbers of houses built in the UK between 1948 and 2003. (b) Brick production over the same period (facing bricks form the outer skin of buildings; commons are lower-quality bricks used internally).

Figure 3.14 confirms the answer to Question 3.2(a), which compares production trends for different kinds of brick with total UK brick production and house-building.

● From the house-building and brick production trends in Figure 3.14, what was the main use for bricks in the UK, and how is this reflected in the graph?

○ The main use was — and still is — house-building. The *demand* for bricks is thus closely dependent on the number of houses being built, and hence the *supply* (essentially, the total production) of bricks matches the trend in house-building. This is an excellent illustration of the variability in demand for building materials.

Question 3.3

(a) Total brick production in the UK was 7200 million bricks in 1960 and 3500 million bricks in 1990 (Figure 3.14). Calculate the percentage of total UK brick production in 1960 and 1990 represented by 'commons'.

(b) Describe the trend in production of facing bricks over the same period (i) in absolute terms; (ii) relative to total UK brick production. (No calculation required.)

(c) What particular case of substitution might explain the contrasting fortunes of 'facing' bricks and 'commons' between 1960 and 1990 in the UK?

The answers to Question 3.3 strongly suggest that the overall decline in UK brick production was due mainly to substitution by other materials. But could there be an underlying, more fundamental, cause? What does the future hold for brick clays in Britain?

3.3.2 The future of brick-making

A decline in the use of a building material could result from depletion of its reserves. Happily, this is not the case with brick clays in the UK: Figure 3.8 shows that there are substantial outcrops of clays suitable for brick-making. Most of these are thick deposits and many outcrops are still available for extraction should demand rise.

● Is there much wastage of raw material in the production of bricks from clay?

○ There is very little waste (< 3% is quoted in Table 2.2), so almost all the clay in the deposits can be used.

However, reserves of specialized clays may be subject to other factors. For instance, the decline of the UK coal industry threatens the supply of 'fireclays', the fossil soils occurring below coal layers and used to make **refractory** products (i.e. those resistant to high temperatures).

More pressing for brick-making in the UK than depletion of reserves are issues such as environmental opposition (to large pits, fossil fuel consumption and emissions), shifts in demand specifications, industry rationalization, and the drive to improve sustainability (e.g. by recycling more brick products). The late 20th century witnessed a change in the structure of the brick industry, with fewer companies operating fewer, more automated, manufacturing sites; many local brickworks ceased production. However, demand for brick clay products has, if anything, diversified, and this effect is compounded by proliferating EU standards and capricious architectural fashions.

● How do these few large manufacturers produce such a wide range of products from a decreasing number of brickworks?

○ Since a wide range of products requires a variety of clays, these must be transported to the brickworks from their sources.

Other environmental issues associated with brick-making include the reduction of emissions from brickworks to meet ever more stringent standards, and sustainability. Since brick is an extremely durable material, it is desirable to encourage re-use of bricks or regeneration of existing buildings rather than wholesale demolition.

3.3.3   Contrasting fortunes: Oxford Clay versus Etruria Marl

Two UK brick clays reflecting the changes in the brick-making industry in contrasting ways are the Jurassic Oxford Clay and the Etruria Marl of Upper Carboniferous age. The Oxford Clay is ideal for large-scale brick-making, with an extensive outcrop (Figure 3.8) and a thick bed of uniform clay easily accessible beneath a thin soil. Its high water content (20%) reduces the amount of water required for easy extrusion of 'green' bricks. In addition, finely dispersed petroleum hydrocarbons in the clay act as a kind of 'internal fuel' during firing, reducing external fuel consumption by the kiln: once the hydrocarbons within the clay begin to burn, the bricks are virtually self-firing. These advantages led to huge numbers of coal-fired kilns becoming established along the outcrop of Oxford Clay in the 19th century, producing mainly common bricks. The Etruria Marl, named after Josiah Wedgwood's factory near Stoke-on-Trent, has a very restricted outcrop by comparison (Figure 3.8), but its high quality makes it suited to the production of engineering bricks, facing bricks, roof tiles and paving, particularly in applications where high-specification materials are required. (The characteristic dark 'Staffordshire Blue' engineering bricks are made from Etruria Marl.)

● What does Figure 3.8 suggest about the number of brickworks sited on these two clays in 1998?

○ Only 2 or 3 works are on the Oxford Clay, but there is a concentration of brickworks on the Etruria Marl around 'The Potteries' near Stoke and around Birmingham.

This pattern highlights the contrasting fortunes of these two brick clays. Demand for common bricks has declined, and coal-fired kilns cannot meet the higher specifications required for facing bricks. Moreover, the hydrocarbons in Oxford Clay actually make the kiln temperature harder to control. So brick production from Oxford Clay decreased markedly from 1970 onwards, while Etruria Marl continued to supply the more stable markets for engineering and facing bricks, as well as diversifying into other products such as tiles. Modern brickworks using Etruria Marl are highly automated, with gas-fired tunnel or down-draught kilns incorporating sophisticated temperature control systems and emission 'scrubbers' that reduce harmful gaseous emissions. Meeting the changing demands of the industry has enabled companies using Etruria Marl to prosper while many Oxford Clay pits have closed. As you will see in Section 3.5, however, even an abandoned clay pit can be a valuable resource.

3.4   Specialist clays: kaolinite and its relatives

Many clays exploited around the world contain kaolinite, named after the Chinese mountain Kaoling, where a pure white clay was first worked to make high-quality porcelain about 500 AD. This association with china goods led to kaolin deposits being dubbed 'china clay' in Britain, but clays containing kaolinite have many other applications besides chinaware.

3.4.1   Occurrence and extraction

China clay (kaolin) is a rock made largely of the mineral kaolinite; once processed, it is also marketed as kaolin. In 1746, deposits of kaolin were discovered in Cornwall by a Plymouth chemist, William Cookworthy, and by the late 18th century kaolin was being shipped to the Wedgwood and Spode potteries in Staffordshire, whence barges returned with coal.

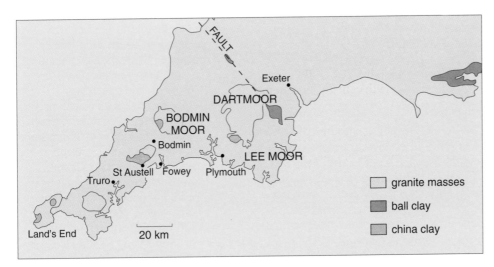

Figure 3.15   China clay and ball clay deposits in southwest England.

In the UK, china clay occurs as small pockets on top of granite bodies in Cornwall and Devon (Figure 3.15). The most valuable (i.e. purest) deposits formed where the granite was poor in iron. Kaolin deposits in the Duvertepe area of northwest Turkey occur along active faults where hydrothermal fluids have altered feldspar-bearing lavas. These deposits are worked in small open pits (Figure 3.16a). Similar processes in western Turkey produced halloysite, a rare 'relative' of kaolinite that has a layer of water molecules separating the aluminosilicate layers. It is used in small quantities mainly for high-quality porcelain manufacture, imparting strength and translucency to delicate ceramic pieces. In these small-scale operations, halloysite is hand-sorted to meet high standards of purity and colour (Figure 3.16b). Since many rich gold deposits are associated with low-temperature hydrothermal systems, kaolin may also be valued as a signpost to possible riches rather than as a resource in its own right!

Figure 3.16   Clay deposits in Turkey: (a) small open pits in kaolin deposits at Duvertepe, northwest Turkey. The deposits follow the trace of a fault that acted as a channel for hydrothermal fluids; (b) hand-sorting of halloysite in western Turkey.

In Cornwall, the second stage of kaolin formation after hydrothermal alteration (Section 3.1.1) was the deep, sub-tropical weathering of the granite in early Tertiary times (~ 50 Ma). This formed isolated pockets of kaolin in the granite by leaching mobile elements (Ca, Na and K) from the hydrothermally altered granite.

● Would you expect these kaolin deposits to contain only kaolinite?

○ No. Although the feldspar in the granite decomposed to form kaolinite, other minerals in the original rock that were not hydrothermally altered or weathered will still be present. These are chiefly quartz and mica.

The final phase in the formation of clays in SW England involved the redistribution of the residual kaolin. In the Tertiary, erosion of the weathered granites and china clay led to kaolinite-rich sediments being laid down in shallow, swampy lakes alongside active faults. The kaolin was mixed with small amounts of material eroded from exposed Devonian and Carboniferous slates to form sediments known locally as 'ball clays' (Figure 3.15). These contain a little illite and quartz in addition to kaolinite. Minor amounts of other impurities (organic matter, pyrite, and other clay minerals) may also be present.

Where eroded kaolinitic material is deposited with little or no other sediment, much higher grade deposits can be formed. Those in Georgia, USA, resulted from erosion of kaolinite-rich laterite formed by tropical weathering of granitic rocks during the Cretaceous and early Tertiary. Transported to the coastal plains, the sedimentary material was then leached again during further weathering, raising the grade of kaolinite even more. Similar leached kaolin deposits occur in the Amazon Basin, Brazil, associated with bauxite deposits. A block diagram summarizing the formation of the different types of kaolin deposit discussed above is shown in Figure 3.17.

Figure 3.17 Model for the processes leading to the formation of different types of kaolin deposit. The sequence of blocks (left to right) represents time passing, as well as spatial separation. In the first block, localized hydrothermal alteration of both granite (location 2, e.g. Cornwall) and overlying, feldspar-rich rocks (location 1, e.g. lavas as in Turkey) forms 'pockets' of kaolin as the granite intrusion crystallizes. Deep, tropical weathering (second block) increases the grade of the kaolin deposits by leaching. This process could affect both kaolin pockets in the granite (location 3) and kaolin-rich sediments (ball clays) that have accumulated in lakes, swamps (location 4), or on coastal plains (as in Georgia, USA). Deposition of the redistributed kaolin, mixed with other clay minerals, may form more extensive ball clay deposits (location 5, third block).

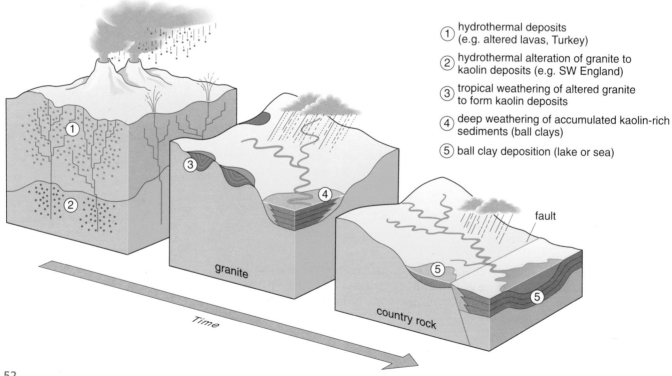

① hydrothermal deposits (e.g. altered lavas, Turkey)

② hydrothermal alteration of granite to kaolin deposits (e.g. SW England)

③ tropical weathering of altered granite to form kaolin deposits

④ deep weathering of accumulated kaolin-rich sediments (ball clays)

⑤ ball clay deposition (lake or sea)

fault

granite

country rock

Time

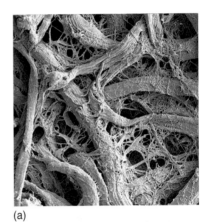

Figure 3.18 A high-pressure hose ('monitor') being used for china clay extraction in Cornwall.

Most kaolin and ball clays are extracted from open pits whose size is ultimately determined by the form of the deposit. China clay in Cornwall is worked using high-pressure water jets called 'monitors' (Figure 3.18) that blast away the rotten granite and carry the clay away in suspension. The clay-rich slurry is channelled down out of the pit and passed through a series of settling tanks, where the coarse quartz and mica settle out. The mica waste still contains significant amounts of kaolinite, which is retrieved by **froth flotation** (the clay particles are preferentially caught up in a foam, which is skimmed off to collect the clay). However, the kaolin still has to go through a succession of size grading, chemical bleaching, magnetic separation and blending procedures before it is suitable for its demanding markets.

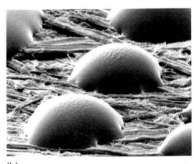

3.4.2 Uses and production

Although known as *china* clay, the main demand for kaolin is in paper manufacture rather than ceramics. Simple paper is composed of a fine mesh of cellulose fibres derived from wood pulp (Figure 3.19a), and is a dull grey colour. Writing or printing on such paper results in 'starring' or blurring of the ink as it is absorbed by the fibres (Figure 3.19d).

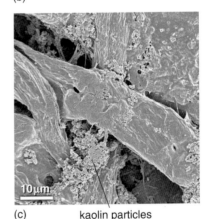

10 µm

(c)   kaolin particles

- How does kaolin help in paper manufacture?

- Firstly, by filling in the holes between the cellulose fibres to reduce absorbency (Figure 3.19b and c), and secondly, by coating the paper with a fine, smooth, white finish which is easy to write or print on.

Figure 3.19 (a) SEM image (180 µm across) of handmade paper with no filler or coating; (b) SEM image of surface of kaolin-filled (but uncoated) plain paper with dots (about 50 µm in diameter) of printer ink also containing kaolin; (c) SEM image of paper, showing small kaolin particles as filler between the fibres; (d) Composite inkjet letter on coated and uncoated paper; ink dots on left about 150 µm in diameter.

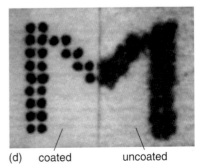

(d)   coated   uncoated

The kaolin filler has a moderately fine grain size (~ 40% of particles are <2 μm in diameter), but the coating is of much higher quality (~ 90% of particles <2 μm). Colour and brightness are also strictly controlled, as are its properties on mixing with water: the coating is applied as a slurry, which must spread evenly. Surprisingly, perhaps, many inks also contain very fine-grained kaolin (Figure 3.19b).

Kaolin is also used as a filler in rubber, plastics and paints, but faces stiff competition from other minerals. For instance, finely ground limestone can substitute for kaolin as a paper coating (Section 4.4.2). Some low-grade kaolin is used in ceramics and white cement.

The main reason china clay is *not* used for delicate ceramics is that, even when mixed with water, it is not easily moulded into a complex shape such as a shepherdess figurine. This property, known as **plasticity**, is more characteristic of ball clays, which are often known as 'plastic clays'. By blending clays of different compositions, a range of ceramic products can be made, such as earthenware, tableware, tiles, sanitaryware, and electrical porcelain (insulators etc.). The UK is among the world leaders in ceramic clay production, but the trend at the turn of the 21st century is to manufacture all but the highest quality products where labour costs are low, for example in the Far East. Initially, the clay was transported to the factories from its traditional sources in Western Europe and the USA, but companies are now investing in ball clay extraction in Thailand, Indonesia and China due to their proximity to the ceramics factories. Hence the UK now imports significant amounts of cheap ceramics from these countries, despite still having some of the world's best raw materials.

3.5 Clay pits: landfill and restoration

One of the pressures of population increase is the generation of vast volumes of waste. In earlier times, the lower volumes of waste produced were disposed of locally and unsystematically, for instance in prehistoric middens. These mounds of discarded food and utensils are studied today by archaeologists for insights into ancient diet and living conditions. Modern consumer societies generate more waste, yet demand more controlled disposal of waste on sanitary and aesthetic grounds, though in many parts of the world more haphazard conditions still exist. Legislation is increasingly used to ensure that our waste has a minimal effect on the environment.

- What are the three main approaches to the disposal of waste?

- Waste can be burnt (incineration), buried (landfilling) or recycled (including composting for biodegradable material).

Incineration is seldom a popular solution with the local residents; it produces emissions that have been linked to health problems as well as greenhouse gases. **Landfilling** (Box 3.2) is defined as 'the controlled deposit of waste on land, in a manner such that pollution or harm is negligible'. The volume of waste has exceeded the capacity of local quarries, which were traditional disposal sites in many parts of the UK. However, many stone quarries are unsuitable for waste disposal due to the risk of groundwater pollution, as discussed in Section 2.5.1.

A site suitable for landfilling must be able to *contain* potential contaminants permanently, and prevent their release into the wider environment (Box 3.3). Apart from the obvious environmental problems of litter, odour and traffic pollution, landfill sites generate two main hazards: **leachate**, and **landfill gas**. Leachate is the liquid that accumulates in a landfill, mainly from rainwater falling on the site and decomposition of the waste itself, but also occasionally from groundwater that accidentally leaks into the site. Leachate can extract undesirable substances from the waste, and is a threat to water supplies if it migrates (see Figure 2.13). Landfill gas is produced when bacteria break down putrescible matter in landfills. It consists mainly of methane and carbon dioxide, plus traces of other (mainly organic) gases; it is potentially explosive and asphyxiating. Since very few wastes, including construction rubble, are truly inert, almost all waste materials generate leachate and landfill gas.

Box 3.2   UK waste production and the Landfill Tax

Table 3.2   Summary of annual UK waste production[*].

	Type of waste						
	Construction/ demolition	Mining, quarrying	Agriculture	Sewage, dredging	Industrial/ commercial	Domestic	Total
Proportion/%	24	21	20	8	19	8	100
Quantity/Mt	104	91	87	35	82	35	434

[*] Figures are estimates based on surveys from 1998–2001.

In the late 1990s, 82% of UK domestic waste was sent to landfill, 10% was recycled or composted, and the remainder was incinerated. It has been estimated that by 2020, £3.2 billion will be spent annually on municipal waste disposal in England alone. A European Union directive in 1996 required a drastic reduction in biodegradable waste sent to landfill by 2020 (to 35% of 1995 levels). As domestic waste is increasing at about 3–4% per year, this is a severe challenge.

●   How might this reduction be effected?

○   The unpopularity of waste incineration means that the more sustainable option of increasing recycling and composting measures is the way forward.

Apart from improving local facilities (e.g. recycling sites, kerbside collection schemes), a major initiative is raising public awareness. The irony is that awareness of the problem is low in modern societies, as waste is removed from the vicinity of the home so efficiently.

Another way to tackle the problem is legislation. In 1996, the UK Government introduced a tax on material sent to landfill, aiming to curb waste production and encourage recycling. The tax rates in 2004 were £2 per tonne for inert waste (e.g. rocks, soils, concrete, glass, furnace slags and power station ash), and £15 per tonne for 'active' waste that breaks down in landfill sites but is not necessarily hazardous, such as household waste. A subsequent report estimated a reduction of ~45% in inert wastes sent to landfill as a result of the tax.

To mitigate the effect of landfill sites on neighbouring communities, landfill operators in the UK can donate a proportion of their landfill tax liability to local environmental projects, in return for a tax credit. By mid 2004, over £500 million had been spent under this scheme on local projects, including recycling initiatives, restoration of historic buildings, and habitat creation.

Box 3.3 Landfill containment

To safeguard underground and surface water quality, landfill sites that accept non-inert waste must be constructed with impermeable liners designed to:

- prevent the escape of leachate to underground or surface waters;
- prevent underground water percolating into the waste to produce more leachate;
- control the migration of landfill gas.

Two types of lining materials can be used to seal sites before filling begins:

- Plastic sheeting, usually high-density polyethylene (HDPE), 2 mm or more in thickness, called a **geomembrane**. The HDPE arrives at the site in rolls about 7 m wide and up to 100 m long; the sheet material has to be joined on-site by special heat-welding techniques (Figure 3.20a).
- Clay, carefully compacted by special machinery until it is 1 m thick and effectively impermeable. Known as a **mineral liner**, this is the same basic technique used 200 years ago to make canals watertight with a 'puddled' layer of clay.

Since landfill sites are sizeable operations, substantial quantities of lining materials are required. Typically, a new landfill site might occupy 10 hectares (1 hectare = 10^4 m^2). This requires 100 000 m^2 of HDPE (at, say, £15 per m^2) or 100 000 m^3 of clay (the cost of which depends on whether suitable clay is present at the site or has to be brought in). Clay is also spread over the top of the compacted waste (Figure 3.20b) to reduce addition of rainwater to the leachate. As the rubbish slowly decomposes, the gas given off may be collected for use as fuel.

These two types of liner may behave differently under a pile of waste many metres in thickness and many tonnes in weight. A split geomembrane or a dried-out clay mineral liner could allow leakage of leachate. Thus, it is now usual to attempt to get the 'best of both worlds' by specifying a composite liner, consisting of a mineral liner overlain by an HDPE geomembrane, but this extra security against leakage of leachate and migration of landfill gas comes at a price. Consequently, in modern engineered landfill sites, the cost of waste disposal has risen substantially.

Figure 3.20 (a) Installing an HDPE membrane to provide an impervious floor to a waste disposal site. (b) Aerial view of Calvert brickworks in Oxford Clay, Buckinghamshire. One of the three more recent excavations in the foreground is partially infilled; in the background are the tall chimneys of the old brickworks just in front of two older, flooded pits. At the time of writing (2004) these host a marina and a nature reserve.

In the past, little regard was paid to leachate or gas control at waste disposal sites. Leachate was generally assumed to become *attenuated* as it percolated down to the water table, i.e. its noxious qualities would be reduced by dilution and a range of complex, natural, physical, chemical and microbiological processes. Concerns about the effectiveness of this *dilute and disperse* approach were raised in the UK in the mid-1980s, when a number of incidents involving migration of gas from landfill sites (through porous strata or other pathways such as underground service pipes) prompted a change in policy to *containment*.

● Why would old clay pits be better suited to the containment approach of landfilling than old stone quarries?

○ Clay is impermeable, so it will help contain leachate and landfill gas within the site. Many building stone quarries, however, are in permeable strata, which would allow contaminating fluids to leak into the subsurface environment.

Containment aims to restrict the migration of leachate and landfill gas by means of an impermeable, basal lining system on which the waste is placed (see Box 3.3). If the base of the site is truly impermeable, all leachate can be collected on-site and treated before disposal. The liner will also confine emissions of gas to the area of the site itself, where it is either vented to the atmosphere via pipes built into the waste or, if sufficient volumes are produced, collected for use as a fuel. Landfill gas is about 60% methane, and so has a high calorific value; in this way, each tonne of waste produces more net energy than if it were burned. In 2001, over 75 of the UK's 500 landfill sites collected methane for use as fuel.

Abandoned clay pits can be put to other uses besides landfill, and may even be a more valuable resource than the extracted clay. Increasingly, restoration is an important part of planning the extraction of any bulk resource, and occurs side by side with extraction to minimize the impact on the landscape. Pits may be infilled, for example with an inert waste material such as pulverized fuel ash (PFA), a by-product of coal-fired power stations, and returned to agricultural use with a covering of topsoil. Flooded pits can become recreational sites or nature reserves (Figure 3.20b). For those abandoned clay pits where no provision was made for their fate beyond extraction, both imagination and investment are needed to address potentially dangerous eyesores. Over 200 years of clay extraction in the area near St Austell in Cornwall has left numerous pits (Figure 3.21a), many of them flooded, as well as vast tips of white waste material. (These tips were formerly known as 'The Cornish Alps' before late 20th century landscaping.) While some of these are still a restoration headache, one disused pit is a striking example of innovative restoration. It now houses the Eden Project, a cluster of huge, climate-controlled greenhouses showcasing plants from different environments around the world (Figure 3.21b).

Figure 3.21 The legacy of kaolin extraction in Cornwall: (a) The Bodelva china clay pit near St Austell, shortly before innovative restoration; (b) The completed Eden Project biomes nestling in the disused pit.

3.6 Summary of Chapter 3

1   Clay minerals are the weathering products of rock-forming minerals such as feldspars, micas and amphiboles. They are a major constituent of clay soils and accumulate in sedimentary basins to form mudstones.

2   Clay is transported as tiny, charged clay particles forming a colloidal suspension in fresh water, and deposited either in quiet water bodies (e.g. lakes) or on entering seawater, when the colloidal particles clump together (flocculate) and settle to the seabed.

3   Clay minerals are complex, layered aluminosilicates, which can be classified into three main groups: kaolinite, illite and smectite.

4   Smectite clays, formed from volcanic ashes, have a range of specialized uses that exploit their unique chemistry, absorbency, and physical properties.

5   The main use of mudstones is to make bricks and other ceramic products for the building industry. Brick products vary widely according to the composition of the raw materials and the firing conditions.

6   Improved, cheaper transport in Victorian Britain led to a boom in building with brick. Substitution by concrete and other modern materials since the mid-1960s has led to a gradual decline in UK brick production.

7   Abundant reserves of brick clays exist in the UK, but production of some clays (e.g. fireclays) may be threatened by indirect factors such as UK coal pit closures.

8   The formation of china clay (kaolin) deposits commonly involves low-temperature hydrothermal alteration of feldspar-bearing rock, as in southwest England, and along active faults in northwest Turkey.

9   Kaolin is an important resource used in many applications, for example as a filler in paper and plastics. Manufacture of many ceramic products from ball clays has been relocated to centres of cheaper labour such as the Far East.

10 Old clay pits are a valuable resource in themselves. The impermeability of clay makes old pits suitable for landfill, although the European Union is trying to reduce landfill usage. More innovative uses include flooding for water amenities, restoration to agriculture or nature reserves, and ventures such as the Eden Project in Cornwall.

LIMESTONE: A VERSATILE RAW MATERIAL

4

One of the most widely used industrial minerals is calcium carbonate ($CaCO_3$), which occurs in many natural forms: coral, seashells (including mother-of-pearl), stalactites, calcite veins, crystalline marble, and even in some igneous rocks. However, it is most familiar as the main constituent of limestone. Limestone is widespread and relatively inexpensive, so it has long been used as a building stone, as well as for making other building materials (e.g. lime mortar). The physical and chemical properties of calcium carbonate, and its availability, mean that it has countless everyday applications, from cosmetics to medicine. However, its main role is in the manufacture of that ubiquitous modern building material, concrete. Before moving on to consider its uses, we will first address the origins of limestone.

4.1 The nature and origins of limestone

Whereas Chapter 3 examined rocks formed of the *insoluble* products of chemical weathering processes (clay minerals), this chapter and the next focus mainly on rocks formed by the precipitation of the *soluble* products of the rock cycle. Such rocks are formed by chemical and biological processes.

● What happens to the calcium, sodium and potassium originally present in feldspars during chemical weathering of granite (Section 3.1.2)?

○ These elements pass into solution as ions (Ca^{2+}, Na^+ and K^+) in the mildly acidic rainwater that breaks down the feldspars and leaves clay mineral residues.

These dissolved ions are carried mainly by rivers to the sea, where they may be precipitated to form **chemical sediments**, defined simply as sediments made up of material precipitated from dissolved ions, by whatever process. Limestones, made up chiefly of calcium carbonate, are the most important chemical sediments. Most limestones are composed wholly or partly of shells and skeletal fragments of calcium carbonate extracted by marine organisms from solution (Figure 4.1a). In fact, when biological processes play an important role in the formation of limestones they may be termed 'biochemical' or 'biogenic' sediments.

Calcium carbonate, dissolved in seawater, is in equilibrium with dissolved carbon dioxide, calcium ions and bicarbonate ions:

$$Ca^{2+} + 2HCO_3^- = CaCO_3 + H_2O + CO_2 \qquad (4.1)$$

calcium ions   bicarbonate ions   calcium carbonate   water   carbon dioxide

Low concentrations of dissolved carbon dioxide (in warm waters – gas solubility decreases with increasing temperature) drive the reaction towards the right-hand side, and can encourage calcium carbonate precipitation without biological help. **Oolitic** limestones (Figure 4.1b) contain small spherical grains called ooids whose appearance suggests direct precipitation: concentric layers of calcium carbonate have built up around tiny particles rolling around on the sea floor. Ooids are currently forming in the warm, shallow seas round the Bahamas; in fact most limestones accumulate on the floors of shallow seas, where they can be very pure

59

(almost 100% $CaCO_3$). More commonly, some clastic material from nearby landmasses is deposited along with the carbonate sediment, resulting in an impure, sandy or muddy limestone.

Limestones are widely distributed across the globe, but there are regions where they are scarce, such as continental interiors dominated by crystalline rocks. In southern Australia, early colonists used calcrete (Box 2.2) as a substitute for limestone. Oceanic islands such as the Maldives, which lack ancient limestones, have had to mine coral reefs for construction materials. On volcanic islands in the South Pacific, modern shell banks and coral or oolitic sands are used instead of limestone as a raw material for cement. By contrast, Britain has abundant limestone deposits of different ages, as shown in Figure 4.2.

If you live on one of the limestone outcrops shown on Figure 4.2, the hardness of the water is a constant reminder of the underlying rock type. Each limestone creates its own distinctive landscape — with numerous clues to its presence.

(a)

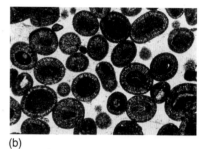
(b)

(c)

(d)

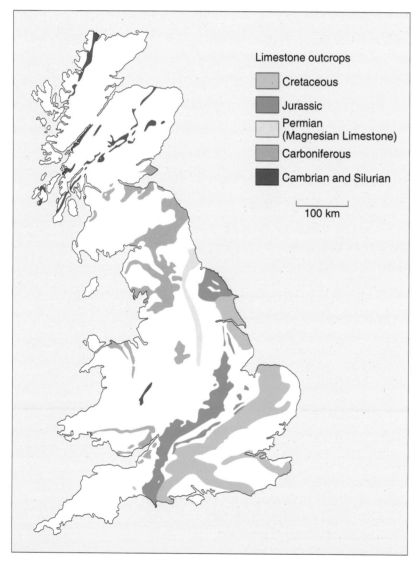

Figure 4.2 Map of Great Britain, showing the main outcrops of limestone divided by age.

Limestone outcrops
- Cretaceous
- Jurassic
- Permian (Magnesian Limestone)
- Carboniferous
- Cambrian and Silurian

100 km

Figure 4.1 Components of limestones: (a) fossiliferous limestone of Carboniferous age, Derbyshire; the rock is made up of the broken remains of reef-dwelling animals, crinoids ('sea lilies'); (b) Jurassic oolitic limestone in thin section showing concentric layers in ooids which are about 0.5 mm across; (c) modern ooids from Salt Lake, Utah (average diameter <0.5 mm); (d) SEM image of coccoliths (each about 5 µm in diameter), the skeletal remains of planktonic organisms, in Cretaceous limestone (Chalk).

Table 4.1   Limestones of Britain.

Geological age	Physical properties	Contains	Distinctive features	Uses
Cretaceous 'Chalk'	soft, porous, fine-grained; bedding indistinct	planktonic remains (Figure 4.1d)	beds of flint nodules; cliffs at Dover; downland pastures; chalk figures	cement-making; lime production
Jurassic 'Oolite'	moderately soft and porous; some well-cemented (e.g. Portland stone); metre-scale bedding	ooids and shelly material	traditional Cotswold building stone; well-drained pastures with lime-loving flora	building stone (some good freestones); some cement-making
Permian 'Magnesian Limestone'	moderately soft and porous; metre-scale bedding	dolomite $(CaMg(CO_3)_2)$	prominent escarpment; rolling hills; lime-loving flora	limited use in refractories, smelting and as a building stone
Carboniferous	tough, well-cemented, low porosity; thickly bedded with many vertical joints	calcareous mud or reef fossils	limestone pavements, caves and potholes (karst topography); limestone walls	roadstone; building stone; cement-making; chemical industry; lime production
Silurian and Cambrian	well-cemented	fossils (e.g. trilobites) locally common	may be altered to marble in Scotland; well-drained pastures	limited or local use, e.g. producing lime

Table 4.1 gives some information on these different limestones, while Figure 4.3 illustrates some distinctive features associated with limestone areas.

Question 4.1

(a) Citing the information in Table 4.1, explain briefly the properties that make Carboniferous and Jurassic limestones more suitable than Chalk as building stone.

(b) Describe how physical toughness and degree of cementation in the limestones in Table 4.1 vary with age, and give a simple reason for this trend.

The three most useful British limestones are the Chalk, and those from the Jurassic and Carboniferous Periods, but they are suited to different applications. In addition, Carboniferous limestone hosts extensive systems of mineralized veins in the UK, which were mined for lead, zinc, silver and iron ores. Nowadays, these veins are exploited for two other minerals: fluorite and barite.

Figure 4.3   Features of limestone areas: (a) Chalk figure — The Long Man of Wilmington, East Sussex; (b) limestone pavement, Cumbria.

Box 4.1   Fluorite: from ornaments to chemicals

Fluorite (CaF_2) is variable in colour, but commonly forms distinctive cubic crystals, which are grown artificially for use as high-quality optical lenses.

In England's Peak District, it also occurs as 'Blue John', a banded purple and yellow form used for ornaments and jewellery (Figure 4.4). Fluorite's other main direct use is as a flux to lower the temperature of various processes (e.g. aluminium and steel smelting). However, most fluorite is used to produce hydrofluoric acid (HF), from which fluorine-based products such as Teflon® (non-stick coatings) are made (Figure 4.5).

Most fluorite occurs in veins with metal ores, precipitated from hydrothermal fluids such as those released when granites crystallize at depth in the crust. As a commodity, fluorite (known by the old term '**fluorspar**') has a relatively low value, which determines how it is extracted. Opencast extraction is favoured, as this incurs less cost, but underground mining may be used for deep veins with more complex geometry. Where fluorite can be extracted together with metal ores, the latter's higher value justifies the greater costs of subsurface mining.

World production of fluorspar is around 4.5 Mt per year, with world reserves estimated at approximately 500 Mt. A minor producer fifteen years ago, China now accounts for between 50% and 70% of world production. The UK produces around 50 000 tonnes of high-grade fluorspar per year. Fluorspar is produced in two forms:

- *metspar*, which is low purity (60–85% CaF_2), used as a flux for various industrial processes;
- *acidspar*, which is high purity (> 97% CaF_2), used as the feedstock for hydrofluoric acid manufacture.

In direct competition with primary fluorspar production is the production of fluorosilicic acid, a waste product of fertilizer manufacture, which can also be used to make fluorine chemicals.

Figure 4.5 shows a dramatic rise in the annual global production of fluorspar during the 1960s, reflecting two major new markets: the manufacture of CFCs (chlorofluorocarbons) as aerosol propellants, and uranium ore processing for nuclear power stations. Environmental concerns relating to ozone depletion with the use of CFCs, and perceived safety problems

Figure 4.4   Ornaments carved from banded fluorite, or 'Blue John'. The height of the tallest pyramid is about 70 mm. (Fluorite crystals are also shown in Figure 4.6a, associated with the mineral barite.)

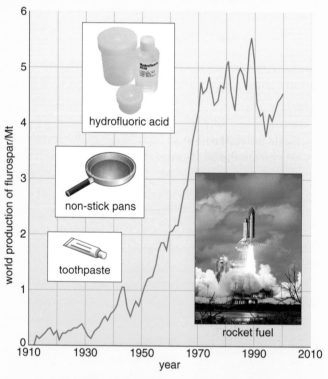

Figure 4.5   World production of fluorspar between 1913 and 2000 (main graph), with some products derived from fluorspar (insets).

with nuclear power, have since curbed both industries. In fact, most aerosols have reverted to the inflammable hydrocarbon-based gases that were considered so dangerous 30 years ago.

Box 4.2 Barite: added weight for industry

In contrast to fluorite, the mineral barite ($BaSO_4$) is used largely for its high density ($4.5\,\mathrm{t\,m^{-3}}$). It typically occurs as crystalline masses (Figure 4.6a) with fluorite and metal ores in veins within Carboniferous limestone, but elsewhere (e.g. Foss mine, Scotland) it may form nodules, massive lenses, or laminated beds (Figure 4.6b) up to 10 m thick in sea-floor sediments. These layered deposits form when barium in hydrothermal fluids reacts with sulphate in seawater to precipitate barite. The Foss deposit is mined underground, but many massive barite deposits outside the UK are extracted from opencast pits.

Figure 4.6 (a) Cream-coloured masses of barite with purple crystals of fluorite. (b) Laminated barite from Foss mine, Scotland.

Barite is soft and variable in colour (commonly white to pink), and is difficult to dissolve in most acids or solvents. However, its high density is the property that distinguishes it from other light-coloured minerals, and its main use is as a weighting agent. During oil well drilling (Figure 4.7a), a bentonite mud is used to lubricate the drill rods in the borehole, lift cuttings from the bottom of the borehole and prevent blowouts. As the hole deepens, addition of barite raises the density of the mud. The amount of barite is adjusted to match the pressure due to any gas, water or oil in reservoirs below, suppressing dangerous blowouts. Barite's softness helps reduce wear on the drill rig.

 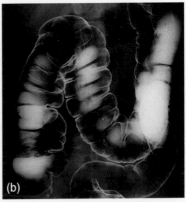

Figure 4.7 Uses for barite: (a) drill rods coated in drilling mud; (b) X-ray image of a human intestine following a 'barium meal' (showing up white).

Barite is used:

- in drilling mud, bowling balls, fillers and concrete because of its *high density*;
- in glass screens (as shielding against X-rays), televisions and computer monitors, intestinal imaging formulations — the 'barium meal' (Figure 4.7b) — because of its *strong X-ray absorption*, and in specialized concrete for storage of radioactive material;
- as a *source of barium chemicals*: white pigments for paints, green firework colourants.

World barite production was around 6 Mt in 2002, dominated by the drilling market (> 5 Mt / annum). Demand for barite is thus closely linked to the level of drilling activity in the petroleum industry, and hence to oil and gas prices. Improvements in drilling technology and seismic subsurface imaging during the late 20th century have reduced the number of wells drilled, with a corresponding fall in demand for barite. In 2002, over 50% of world production was from China, rising dramatically from 16% in 1985. Production in other countries follows the drilling activity of international oil companies: those barite mines closest to new major oil and gas basins have a delivery cost advantage over more distant producers. As drilling moves to new areas these mines may, in their turn, decline.

4.2 Raw materials for cement-making

The peculiar properties of **cement** — a substance that when mixed with water will eventually set to form a hard, rock-like mass — were discovered by the Ancient Greeks, but it was the Romans who first used cement extensively in buildings for binding rock and mineral fragments to make concrete. Three essential ingredients are needed to make cement: calcium carbonate ($CaCO_3$), silica (SiO_2), and alumina (Al_2O_3), as well as a little iron. Conveniently, all of these can be assembled by mixing two common rocks — limestone (for $CaCO_3$), and mudstone (for SiO_2 and Al_2O_3).

4.2.1 Limestone

Some impure limestones contain quartz (silica), clay minerals and some iron as well as calcium carbonate, which would seem ideal for cement-making; indeed such rocks were often known as 'cementstones'. However, the composition of any rock varies even within a single bed, and modern cement plants require raw materials whose compositions are strictly regulated to ensure the correct mix of chemical ingredients. For instance, the Magnesian Limestone of Permian age in the UK is unsuitable for cement manufacture because even relatively minor amounts of magnesium in the cement mix drastically weaken the cement. Purer limestones of more consistent composition are therefore favoured, and the correct chemical mixture is achieved by monitoring the raw materials, and using an appropriate amount of other ingredients such as mudstone. Since limestone generally comprises 70–90% of the mixture, it has the greater influence on the siting of cement works.

The amount of limestone used for cement production in the UK is less than 25% of the limestone quarried each year, but there is no realistic prospect of the raw materials for cement production being in short supply, especially as cement is a relatively high-value limestone product. On the other hand, with the increasing shipment of cargoes around the world in bulk carriers, there is probably a much greater threat to UK cement production from cheap imports than from shortages of supply at home.

4.2.2 Mudstone

To increase the proportion of silica and alumina in the cement mix, a mudstone such as shale or clay must be added to the limestone. In the absence of cementstone, cement works are normally built where suitable limestone and mudstone outcrop next to each other, for instance on the boundary between the Chalk and underlying clay in southern England. The Chalk and clay from opposite ends of the quarry can then be mixed in the correct proportions for the kiln. There is usually around 10–20% mudstone in the mixture, often with other additives (Section 4.3.2). Another common situation is where limestone and shale are interbedded and more than one limestone is worked for cement as well as shale as shown in Figure 4.8, at the Dunbar quarry, Scotland. This diagram also shows how wastes are tipped as the working face advances, so rapid restoration accompanies the quarrying operation, rather like opencast working of coal.

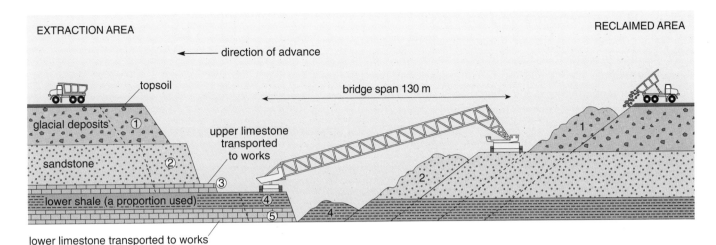

Figure 4.8 Limestones and shales for cement-making: cross-section of a cement quarry near Dunbar, Scotland, where beds of shale and two limestones are worked together. The circled numbers indicate the blocks of strata before extraction; uncircled numbers indicate the corresponding layers of backfill. The bridge conveys rock waste from the working face to the area of reclamation.

4.3 Cement manufacture

Evidence of the Romans' use of concrete remains to this day (e.g. the Pantheon dome, Rome, Figure 4.9a), but after Roman times the secret of cement was lost. It was not until 1756, when John Smeaton built the Eddystone lighthouse (Figure 4.9b) using a mixture of fired ground limestone and clay, which he found would set hard even under water, that cement technology was rediscovered. Cement was patented in 1824 by Joseph Aspdin, who called it Portland cement, because he thought that his cement looked rather like Jurassic limestone from Portland, Dorset, which was then in common use as a building stone. This is the main type of cement used today, and is still called 'OPC' (ordinary Portland cement).

(a)   (b)

Figure 4.9 Examples of concrete structures: (a) the dome of the Pantheon in Rome, built between 118 AD and 128 AD, which has a span of 43 m; (b) the Eddystone lighthouse built by John Smeaton in 1756.

4.3.1 The cement-making process

The basic process is very simple: limestone and clay or shale are mixed together, and then fired in a kiln to a temperature of about 1400 °C. In practice, several stages of crushing, drying, mixing and milling are involved (Figure 4.10) to ensure a fine, well-mixed powder is introduced to the kiln. This increases the efficiency of the reactions that take place. During firing, water vapour is given off first (**dehydration**), followed by CO_2 (**decarbonation**), indicating the decomposition of first the shale and then the limestone to a mixture of anhydrous compounds known as **cement clinker**. The four principal compounds in Portland cement are listed in Table 4.2, with their typical proportions in cement as percentages.

Table 4.2 Compounds in ordinary Portland cement.

Compound	Formula	Percentage
tricalcium silicate	$3CaO.SiO_2$	50–75%
dicalcium silicate	$2CaO.SiO_2$	15–30%
tricalcium aluminate	$3CaO.Al_2O_3$	5–10%
tetracalcium aluminoferrite	$4CaO.Al_2O_3.Fe_2O_3$	5–15%

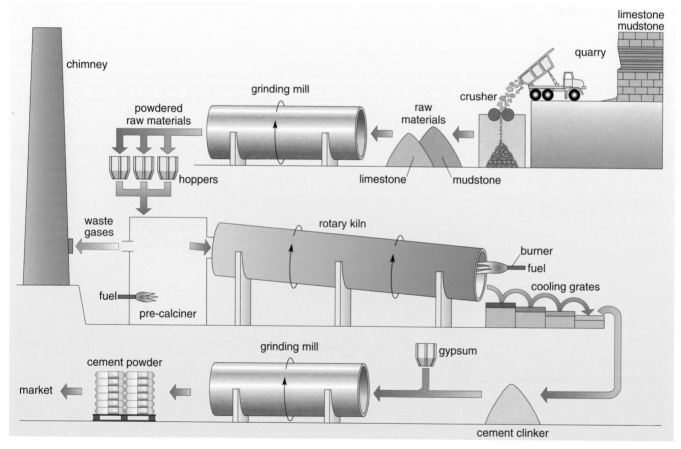

Figure 4.10   Flow diagram for cement manufacture, from extraction of the raw materials (limestone and mudstone, top right), to cement powder ready for the market (lower left). Limestone and mudstone are crushed and ground to fine powders that are easy to blend and quick to react in the kiln. This rock dust is blown into the pre-calciner, a chamber where the material is pre-heated before it passes into the main rotary kiln. Cement-forming reactions occur in sequence as the heat intensifies nearer the burner (lower right). The cement clinker is then cooled, gypsum is added, and the mixture is ground to fine cement powder, which is the final product.

The cement clinker is ground to a powder to produce OPC. Adding water to cement powder forms new hydrated minerals, which grow as long crystals, locking the cement and any inert particles present into a hard mass (Figure 4.11). This process is known as 'setting'.

● Do these hydration reactions (i.e. setting) happen rapidly?

○ No, setting occurs over a prolonged period.

In fact, each reaction has a different rate, with even the quickest reaction lasting a few hours, so cement does not set immediately. Cement needs to be kept moist while hydration is ongoing because water is required for the hydration reactions. Although Portland cement begins to harden in a few hours after mixing, due mainly to the rapid growth of hydrated tricalcium aluminate, the real strength of cement builds up over a few days when the more abundant hydrated tricalcium silicate forms, reaching about 70% of its final strength in a month (Figure 4.12). However, cement does not reach its full strength for several years, as dicalcium silicate hydrates only very slowly. Just because cement or concrete is 'set' does not mean you can treat it as fully hardened and ready to be walked on or driven over.

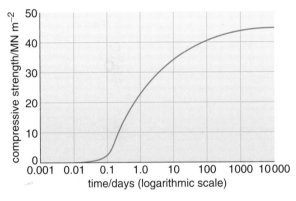

Figure 4.12 Setting of cement, showing crushing strength increasing with time after the addition of water to cement powder. Note that time is shown on a logarithmic scale, whereas the vertical scale (strength in compression) is linear. (The units MN m^{-2} are explained in Box 4.4.)

The reactions that occur as cement hardens are complex and, crucially, *non-reversible*, so that once cement has set, the new hydrated compounds that have formed cannot change back to the anhydrous minerals present in the cement clinker. However, the setting of cement — and other properties — can be modified using various additives (Box 4.3) such as gypsum, which is added to most cement.

Question 4.2

(a) After 3 months' setting, what is the compressive strength of cement?

(b) How old is the cement before it reaches its full compressive strength, and what is this value?

0.005 mm

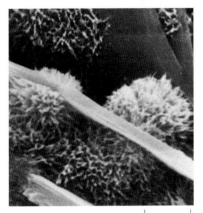

0.005 mm

0.005 mm

Figure 4.11 Growth of crystals in cement to make an 'artificial rock': (a) early needles on cement grains; (b) cement grain covered with fibres of gel and two rod-like crystals; (c) final mass of interlocking fibres.

Box 4.3 Additives for cement

There are three reasons why additional components may be required in cement:

- to make up for a deficiency in one or more of the essential chemical constituents;
- to bulk out the cement mix with cheap filler;
- to modify the properties of the cement.

Some examples of additives are given in Table 4.3.

Blast furnace slag (Table 4.3) is composed mainly of calcium silicates and aluminates, chemically similar to cement, and is a strong pozzolan (a substance that sets with water, named after a fine volcanic ash, *pozzolana,* that the Romans used in cement).

Increasingly, the slag is blended with cement (as powder) or concrete, instead of being simply dumped.

Sulphate-resistant cement (Table 4.3) is designed to counter the adverse effects of excess sulphates in groundwaters or soils that would react with cement, causing swelling and failure of concrete structures. Sulphate-resistant cement is also used in situations where contact with seawater is likely, such as breakwaters. Alkaline solutions produced during cement formation (or from other sources, e.g. groundwater, seawater) may react with certain types of aggregate (Section 6.6.2), causing expansion of concrete and cracking.

Table 4.3 Additional ingredients in cement manufacture.

Component	Reason for additive	Explanation
sand	deficiency	used when mix is poor in silica
pulverized fuel ash[*]	filler/modifier	for a cheaper product, and to lower the alkali content of cement
blast furnace slag	filler/modifier	for a cheaper product, and to lower the alkali content of cement
high-iron clay	modifier	to produce sulphate-resistant cement (see accompanying text)
gypsum	modifier	to slow down the setting rate of the cement
bauxite and/or fluorite	modifier	for quick-setting cement

[*] Pulverized fuel ash (PFA, also known as 'fly ash') is a waste product of coal-fired power stations.

4.3.2 Wastes and emissions

Cement manufacture generates very little waste after quarrying the raw materials — in fact industrial waste materials are increasingly used in making cement. Pulverized fuel ash is a waste material produced in huge quantities by power stations — around 600 Mt were produced globally in 2000 — and its disposal can be a problem. However, it can be added to cement, and used as a filler in concrete, without compromising specifications; in addition it reduces costs significantly. The bulk of the costs involved in cement-making, however, is in the fuel for the rotating kilns that produce the cement clinker, and the various mills and grinders used to pulverize and mix both raw materials and products (Figure 4.10). This has led to the use of a variety of waste products (used tyres, spent motor oil, printing ink, industrial solvents) as fuel. A typical cement plant can burn over one million tyres in a year, and such measures can lead to a considerable reduction in waste that would otherwise be sent to landfill.

● What detrimental effect might this use of waste as fuel have on the environment?

○ Increased emissions of gaseous pollutants, including the greenhouse gas CO_2.

It is estimated that 8% of all anthropogenic CO_2 emissions worldwide are due to the manufacture of cement — on top of fuel emissions, the formation of the calcium silicates in cement *also* produces large volumes of CO_2 by decarbonation. The net effect is that for every tonne of cement produced, over 1 tonne of CO_2 is released. Certain fuels that emit less CO_2 (e.g. natural gas, agricultural waste) could reduce these emissions. In fact the high kiln temperatures promote almost total combustion of wastes, resulting in very low emission levels — much lower than municipal waste incinerators. So, while improvements in the process may reduce energy requirements, CO_2 emissions are unavoidable and will inevitably remain high, a problem for countries committed to reducing greenhouse gas emissions by treaties such as the Kyoto Protocol (1997).

4.4 Cement consumption and production

4.4.1 Uses of cement

Cement is generally mixed with some kind of aggregate (sand, gravel or crushed rock fragments) to form a variety of building materials. Mortar, made from a mixture of cement and sand, bonds the bricks in a wall together; floor screeds are of a similar mix. For mortar, 1 part by volume of cement powder is mixed with 3 to 6 parts by volume of sand, with enough water to make the paste workable — some lime is commonly added to improve plasticity and workability. A thin skin of a similar cement–sand mix known as render is used on external walls. This is often applied to wire mesh on a timber framework in the USA. Somewhat reminiscent of medieval 'wattle and daub' walls made of clay and straw, rendering is perhaps more fragile, but quick and cheap. However, most cement is mixed with coarser aggregate as well as sand to make concrete. This is perhaps the most important modern building material, and the latest cheap, bulk building material that humankind has substituted for natural stone. Many houses built in the UK during the early 21st century are founded on concrete, roofed with concrete tiles, and have load-bearing internal walls of lightweight concrete blocks bound with mortar. It is vital for such a material to be strong, but Figure 4.13 shows that we need not always sacrifice beauty for strength.

(a)

(b)

(c)

Figure 4.13 Examples of concrete structures:
(a) Sydney Opera House, Australia, which is tiled in concrete;
(b) the concrete cows, Milton Keynes, UK, designed by Liz Leyh;
(c) skyscraper in Riyadh, Saudi Arabia, for which concrete was mixed with crushed ice instead of water to keep it cool in high daytime temperatures and prevent it setting too quickly.

Box 4.4   The compressive strength of building materials

Any building material, such as a brick in a wall or concrete foundations, must bear the weight of the overlying structure — and in some cases it must also bear additional loads (such as road traffic). A vital property of these materials is their resistance to being crushed — their **crushing** or **compressive strength** — which can be thought of as a pressure, i.e. *force per unit area*.

The scientific (SI) unit of force is the **newton (N)**, named after Sir Isaac Newton. Appropriately enough, it represents the force of gravity acting on the mass of a typical apple, about 0.1 kg. The SI unit of pressure (force per unit area) is the pascal (Pa). One pascal is equal to the force of one newton acting over one square metre ($1\,Pa = 1\,N\,m^{-2}$). Since this is much too small a pressure to be useful in testing materials, compressive strength is usually measured in units of meganewtons ($10^6\,N$) per square metre (written as $MN\,m^{-2}$) as in Figure 4.12.

The crushing strength of rocks (e.g. Table 4.4) varies widely, typically from around $10\,MN\,m^{-2}$ for a soft limestone up to $350\,MN\,m^{-2}$ for some crystalline igneous rocks or quartzites. Carboniferous limestone is among the strongest of sedimentary rocks, approaching $100\,MN\,m^{-2}$. Chapter 6 examines this property in more detail, in relation to aggregates for roadbeds.

To ensure they meet specifications, artificial materials such as concrete are tested using cubes that are cast specially for the purpose. These are crushed to destruction in a large press, normally 28 days after mixing the cement to allow for setting; typical values lie in the range $20–40\,MN\,m^{-2}$. When the test cubes do not come up to strength, concrete used for structural purposes has to be demolished and new material cast.

Table 4.4   Compressive strengths of some building materials.

Material	Locality	Age	Compressive strength /$MN\,m^{-2}$
building stones:			
Bath limestone	Bath, UK	Jurassic	18–25
Portland limestone	Portland, UK	Jurassic	30–41
Penrith sandstone	Lazonby, UK	Permian	93–118
Orton Scar limestone	Orton, UK	Carboniferous	95
Carrara marble	Alpe Apuane, Italy	Jurassic	90–130
'Imperial Black' gabbro	Adelaide, S. Australia	Ordovician	217
bricks:			
common			5–35
engineering			70
mortar			5–15
concrete			15–125
steel (reinforcing rods)			520
wood			30–70

Question 4.3

With reference to Table 4.4, answer the following:

(a) Which of the following materials would an engineer favour — purely on the basis of strength — for a set of massive columns supporting a heavy roof?

  Portland limestone   common bricks   Carrara marble

(b) Suggest a reason why engineering bricks might be chosen over Orton Scar limestone to build an arched bridge over a busy railway in an industrial city, despite the fact that the limestone is the stronger material. (Ignore the economic factors.)

'Ready-mix' concrete can be poured straight from a rotating drum mounted on a truck, for use as fills and foundations, but must be used within about 2 hours of adding water, in case it sets. Other forms of concrete include masonry blocks, which can be cast in any shape for specific architectural uses, and precast concrete in forms such as girders, pipes and slabs, which are cast in a factory and assembled on the construction site. Different applications demand different specifications: a trench-fill mix must flow easily to fill a void efficiently, but need not be very strong, whereas high-rise buildings require concrete with a very high compressive strength. Concrete exposed to frost, such as in paving slabs, has air bubbles deliberately entrained within it. These pores allow freeze–thaw processes to operate within the concrete without damaging its structure. Some lightweight concrete is honeycombed with tiny pores, a texture that can be achieved by mixing cement with foam. Lightweight blocks made in this way have many advantages:

- their low density means that larger blocks can be handled easily;
- they provide good thermal and sound insulation.

How does cement compare to other building materials in terms of cost? Estimates suggest that producing 1 tonne of cement consumes around 2.5 times more energy than producing 1 tonne of bricks, so in terms of energy consumption by weight, cement is more costly.

● Why is this not a fair comparison of the total costs of *building* a cement wall or a brick wall?

○ A wall cannot be made with bricks alone — some cement must also be used to make the mortar that binds the bricks together. Also, cement is not used as a building material by itself, but for normal purposes is mixed with between 4 and 10 times its weight of cheaper materials (aggregate, sand, PFA). So one tonne of cement contributes to many tonnes of finished product.

Thus cement-based materials like concrete are generally cheaper than bricks when the tonnage of *finished* structure is considered, and even cheaper if compared *per cubic metre*.

Table 4.5 gives some typical retail costs of building materials.

Table 4.5   Comparative costs of building materials (local retail prices, early 2000s).

Material	Cost	Cost/£ t^{-1}	Density/t m^{-3}	Cost/£ m^{-3}
common bricks	£28 per 100	115	1.7	
facing bricks	£40 per 100	172	2.0	
handmade bricks	£45 per 100	193	1.8	
cement blocks (= 6 bricks*)	£7.95 per m^2	61	1.3	
lightweight blocks† (= 6 bricks*)	£8.25 per m^2	165	0.5	
aggregate or sand	—	12	1.9	
cement	£3.12 for 25 kg	125	not relevant	not relevant
ready-mix concrete	—	25	2.4	60

* Cement and insulating blocks occupy the same volume in a wall as 6 bricks.

† Low-density blocks used for their good insulating properties.

Question 4.4

(a) Complete the final column of Table 4.5 (ready-mix concrete has been done already).

(b) Of the materials listed in Table 4.5, which is the cheapest by volume for building a small wall?

(c) Would the material you selected for part (b) be the most *cost-effective* material for the inner skin of a house wall? If not, suggest which material(s) you would consider as an alternative.

4.4.2 Cement production

In 2001, global production of cement was roughly 1.7 billion tonnes. About twice as much concrete was used in construction worldwide as that used in *total* for all other building materials. The multitude of uses already mentioned for cement implies that this material and its derivatives have substituted extensively for other building materials in the 20th century — notably brick-clay products, as discussed in the last section.

⬤ Do the production trends for cement bear out this theory? (Compare Figure 4.14 with Figure 3.14 showing brick production.)

◯ Inspection of the graphs confirms the suggestion that bricks have lost market share to concrete in the UK during the period 1960 to 2002.

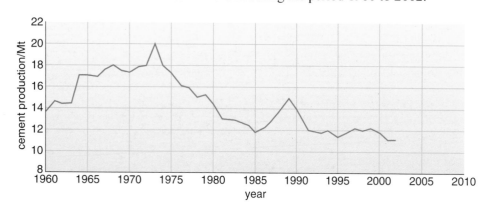

Figure 4.14 Annual cement production in Britain between 1960 and 2002.

In fact Figure 4.14 does not tell the full story, because whereas only about half a million tonnes of cement a year were imported into the UK before the 1980s, that figure had risen to almost 2.5 million tonnes in 2002, as cement was increasingly traded on the international market. On the other hand, the UK still produces the bulk of its own bricks.

4.5 Other applications of calcium carbonate

So far in this book, limestone has been portrayed as an important construction material (either as dimension stone or in concrete); it is also widely used in aggregate (Chapter 6). The following section explores a few of the numerous other ways that calcium carbonate contributes to our daily lives, via agriculture and industry.

4.5.1 Sources and processing

Calcium carbonate in the UK is derived mainly from sedimentary limestone, but worldwide a variety of sources are exploited for calcium carbonate. Marbles are quarried in high-grade metamorphic terrains where younger limestones are absent. Rare igneous rocks called carbonatites, which erupt as lavas in rift zones such as eastern Africa, are also used as a source of calcium carbonate. In some places, hydrothermal veins of coarsely crystalline calcite are also worked, such as those once mined for lead in the English Peak District — the same suite of veins that contain fluorite (Box 4.1).

Limestone itself also has a range of applications apart from cement-making and use as a building stone. Most of these uses demand much higher levels of purity than cement manufacture, requiring careful selection of the purest limestone. In many cases the rock is simply ground to a very fine powder before it is used. One process where purity is important is in the firing of limestone to produce **lime** (calcium oxide, CaO, also called quicklime or burnt lime). Traditionally, this process took place in local lime kilns (Figure 4.15a), but in developed countries these have been replaced by rotary kilns (Figure 4.15b): long, gently inclined, rotating steel tubes with a burner jet at one end. The limestone passes through successively higher temperatures up to around 1000 °C as it moves towards the burner. During the process, CO_2 is lost and quicklime is formed:

$$CaCO_3 + heat = CaO + CO_2 \qquad\qquad (4.2)$$

calcium carbonate   calcium oxide   carbon dioxide

○ Is the decomposition of limestone to produce quicklime (Equation 4.2) exothermic (generating heat) or endothermic (consuming heat)?

○ Additional heat is needed for the reaction to progress, so the decomposition of limestone is *endothermic*.

This property has led to the use of limestone dust throughout coal mines as an explosion retardant. In an underground methane explosion, the fine limestone dust is caught up with the moving flame and is broken down (Equation 4.2), absorbing so much heat that the explosion cannot propagate through the workings. This limestone dust is a potential lifesaver.

Figure 4.15 (a) Traditional lime kiln, Westmorland, England. Local limestone was loaded from the top, and roasted to quicklime (CaO) by a fire stoked below. (b) Modern rotary lime kilns operate in a similar fashion to cement kilns (Figure 4.10).

Quicklime is quite reactive, readily combining with other compounds such as water, but if limestone is fired too hot or too long in the kiln, the lime becomes dense and non-reactive. This 'dead-burned lime' can be used, for example, in the refractories industry. When quicklime reacts with water in an *exothermic* reaction, calcium hydroxide (also called 'slaked' or 'hydrated' lime) is formed:

$$CaO + H_2O = Ca(OH)_2 + heat \qquad (4.3)$$

calcium   water   calcium
oxide   hydroxide

If the calcium hydroxide reacts with CO_2, it can form calcium carbonate and the process has gone full circle:

$$Ca(OH)_2 + CO_2 = CaCO_3 + H_2O \qquad (4.4)$$

calcium   carbon   calcium   water
hydroxide dioxide carbonate

Several calcium compounds are used in industry and agriculture and, as each is known by more than one name, you may find Table 4.6 helpful.

Table 4.6 Chemical and common names of calcium compounds used in building materials.

Chemical name	Common names	Formula
calcium carbonate	limestone, chalk, calcite	$CaCO_3$
calcium oxide	lime, quicklime, roasted limestone, burnt lime	CaO
calcium hydroxide	slaked lime	$Ca(OH)_2$

Reactions such as the one shown in Equation 4.4 are increasingly used to produce precipitated calcium carbonate in a carefully controlled process to give grains of specific size and shape as required for high-value filler applications. These precipitates compete with ultrafine powders produced by simply grinding suitable natural limestones (e.g. Cretaceous Chalk). The coccolith skeletons that make up the bulk of the Chalk (Figure 4.1d) are easy to disaggregate, white in colour and chemically quite pure — an easy starting material from which to produce fine powders economically.

4.5.2 Products and derivatives

Uses of lime

Bricks and stone have been bonded with mortar since at least 7000 BC, long before cement was discovered. A **lime mortar** made by mixing lime and sand was commonly used instead, as in Neolithic Catal Hüyuk (Figure 1.2); Conwy Castle in Wales had a gleaming surface coat of lime mortar (Figure 4.16). You may have noticed that the mortar in many old walls is much softer, and often a paler, creamier colour, than modern cement mortar. Widespread well into the 19th century, lime mortar is now specified for conservation work on heritage buildings. Some argue that one reason why older buildings seem to 'bear their age with grace' is that lime mortar, being much less rigid than the stone, enables a building to 'give' a little by allowing small movements in the soft mortar layers, thus preventing major cracks developing through the stone or bricks. This in turn makes recycling of the bricks or stone easier.

Figure 4.16 Relics of medieval lime mortar on the wall of Conwy Castle, North Wales. Most of Edward I's famous castles had their walls rendered in this way to emphasize their symbolic hold over the country.

Figure 4.17 Lime for the environment: addition of lime to a lake reduces water acidity due to acid rain.

Quicklime is the starting point for manufacture of most calcium-based chemicals, and its ability to neutralize acid solutions finds widespread use in the chemical industry. This neutralizing ability also has important environmental applications, such as raising the pH of waters affected by either acid rain or acid mine drainage (Figure 4.17). Water seeping through old mines is often not only acidic, but also contains toxic heavy metals (e.g. cadmium); lime helps suspended solids to settle out, trapping the toxic metals in the resultant sludge and preventing their release into nearby streams. Similar processes are used in the treatment of drinking water, and waste water from sewage and industrial plants.

Uses of limestone

Limestone has long been used in iron and steel smelting as a flux to lower the melting temperature of the raw materials and to scavenge impurities from the ore. Limestone is the main raw material for making soda ash (Na_2CO_3), an important component in making glass. It is also used to clean up exhaust gases from coal-fired power stations and brickworks. Pollutants such as sulphur, chlorine and fluorine in these gases react with powders or chippings of limestone (or hydrated lime) in chambers known as 'scrubbers'. One useful by-product of this process is calcium sulphate (gypsum), which you will encounter again in the next chapter.

Relatively pure, white limestones are widely used in ultrafine powder-form as fillers for rubber, plastics, papers and paints (Table 4.7). The basic purpose of fillers is to add passive bulk to the product.

Table 4.7 Applications of calcium carbonate fillers and their properties.

Application	Example	Important property
provide bulk to product (thereby reducing costs)	numerous plastics etc.	inexpensive material
reduce need for costly white pigments (e.g. TiO_2)	plastics, paints*, paper	colour, purity
add weight to product	carpet backing	density
improve rigidity	household plastics	strength
improve impact strength	car bumpers	strength

* White lines on UK roads are made brighter and more reflective by adding crystalline calcite to the paint.

● Which do you think would be more important for choosing a filler: its physical or its chemical properties?

○ In general, physical properties are more important than chemical properties for filler selection; the single most important chemical property is being inert with respect to the host material.

The way a filler performs is determined by, amongst others, the particle size distribution of the powder, the shape of the grains, its porosity, and its surface properties that control its ability to bond with the other components in the mixtures. Some fillers are coated with chemicals that improve the bond between the filler and organic components (solvents, polymers and resins), to enhance the strength of the products. In paper-making, some or all of the filling and coating clays can be substituted by the use of extremely fine-grained calcium carbonate. For high-quality paper and plastics applications, precipitated $CaCO_3$ is frequently used because the size and shape of the crystallized particles can be tailored to the needs of the target market.

When we take medicinal pills, the active drugs are present in only milligram proportions. A tablet made only of the pure drug would be too small to pick up, and you would not be sure if you had swallowed it! Calcium carbonate is often impregnated with drugs to form tablets of a more manageable size.

● What chemical property of calcium carbonate ensures that we can take such tablets safely?

○ It is non-toxic to humans.

Provided it is free from harmful impurities, calcium carbonate is easily tolerated by the body and can actually be beneficial, so it is widely used in foods and vitamin supplements as well as in pharmaceutical products. The 'added calcium' advertised in many foods is often incorporated by adding hydrated lime or limestone — this includes many breakfast cereals, dairy products and flour. Even indigestion can be combated by tablets containing calcium carbonate. Many foodstuff production processes also need calcium carbonate: it is used to make sodium bicarbonate (baking soda); in sugar-refining it neutralizes and clarifies the product; while in brewing it is a common pH regulator.

It is not just humans that benefit from a dose of calcium carbonate. Animal feed is a major user of limestone; as is poultry grit, used to ensure that egg-laying hens produce thick and strong shells for their eggs. Agriculture uses powdered limestone (as well as slaked lime and quicklime) for regulating soil pH, and as a fertilizer, particularly in the forestry sector.

Calcium carbonate is not only good for us on the inside: it is also used as a carrier for cosmetics with strong colour tints. Powdered limestone is found in many lipsticks, eye shadows and liners, and foundation creams. These 'sophisticated' embellishments thus have a lot in common with earth pigments used for facial decoration by tribal peoples. Many baby powders (i.e. talcum powder) contain large amounts of limestone as well as the mineral talc. Domestically, limestone is also found in the scouring creams and polishes we use, acting as a mild abrasive — just as it does in some types of toothpaste.

4.6 Summary of Chapter 4

1   Limestone is the most abundant form of calcium carbonate. A widespread rock type, it has a long history of exploitation, and numerous uses.

2   Most limestones owe their existence to chemical or biochemical processes as much as to physical sedimentation.

3   There are three principal limestones exploited in the UK: the Cretaceous Chalk, Jurassic oolite, and Carboniferous limestone. The latter hosts veins containing the minerals fluorite and barite, which are also important industrial minerals.

4   Limestone is an essential raw material for cement, and hence concrete — the most widely used building material of the modern world.

5   A variety of additional components, including industrial wastes, may be added to cement either as bulk or to modify its properties.

6   Cement manufacture involves heating the raw materials to high temperatures, which consumes significant amounts of fuel. Both fuel combustion and decarbonation of limestone during firing generate large volumes of CO_2 emissions, contributing to global warming.

7   The low cost and versatility of concrete has resulted in it substituting for many other building materials, notably bricks, in the latter half of the 20th century.

8   Limestone is also burnt to make lime, used as a filler, and employed in countless industrial applications from iron smelting to cosmetics.

MINERALS: BULK MATERIALS FOR BUILDING AND INDUSTRY

EVAPORITES: SALTS OF THE EARTH

The term **evaporite** refers to a group of minerals that form by crystallization from a salty solution such as seawater as water evaporates. They are chemically diverse but share the ability to be water-soluble under conditions commonly found at or near the Earth's surface. They are typically metal halides, but include sulphates and borates as well. They are the most important source of elements such as lithium, boron and strontium but are most widely exploited for bulk industrial mineral commodities such as gypsum, potash and salt.

5.1 Formation of evaporite deposits

Seawater contains dissolved quantities of most elements, many originally derived from the weathering of crustal rocks, especially the more soluble metal ions, which entered solution as a result of the chemical weathering of minerals such as feldspars (Section 3.1.2, Figure 3.2). The concentration of these ions in river water is very low, often less than 120 milligrams per litre ($mg\,l^{-1}$) in total, but over geological time vast amounts of metal ions have been carried by the world's rivers from the land to the sea, where they have been concentrated by continuous evaporation of water. In contrast, much of the chloride and bromide (and some of the carbonate) in seawater is derived from volcanic gases from either continental volcanoes or submarine vents. Table 5.1 lists the constituents of seawater present in concentrations of more than $1\,mg\,l^{-1}$; each litre of seawater typically contains about 35 g of dissolved salts. Because of the amount of water in the oceans, the amounts of elements present in minute concentrations in seawater can still add up to huge quantities overall. However, sodium, chlorine, magnesium and bromine are the only elements to be extracted commercially from the oceans today.

Table 5.1 The abundance of dissolved elements in seawater, and the salts precipitated on evaporation.

Element	Common dissolved species	Concentration of element/ $mg\,l^{-1}$ *	Salt formed on evaporation	% by weight of salt formed on total evaporation
chlorine (Cl)	Cl^-	1.95×10^4	NaCl	78.04
sodium (Na)	Na^+	1.08×10^4	$MgCl_2$	9.21
magnesium (Mg)	Mg^{2+}	1.29×10^3	$MgSO_4$	6.53
sulphur (S)	SO_4^{2-}	9.05×10^2	$CaSO_4.2H_2O$	3.48
calcium (Ca)	Ca^{2+}	4.12×10^2	$CaCO_3$	0.33
potassium (K)	K^+	3.80×10^2	KCl	2.11
bromine (Br)	Br^-	67	$MgBr_2$	0.25
carbon (C)	HCO_3^-, CO_3^{2-}	28		
strontium (Sr)	Sr^{2+}	8		
boron (B)	$B(OH)_3, B(OH)_4^-$	4.4		
silicon (Si)	$Si(OH)_4$	2		
fluorine (F)	F^-	1.3		
total dissolved salts		$35\,000^\dagger$		

* $mg\,l^{-1}$ (mg per litre) is equivalent to ppm (parts per million).
† Total dissolved salts in seawater = 3.5% by weight (elements at $<1\,mg\,l^{-1}$ are omitted).

Seawater represents a vast, accessible resource of some elements, such as magnesium. Although present in seawater at a concentration of ~ 0.1% by weight, which is only about one-hundredth of its concentration in common rocks like dolomite (a calcium–magnesium carbonate rock), it is cheaper to extract magnesium from seawater than from this rock. The reason is that it is relatively easy to precipitate magnesium hydroxide, $Mg(OH)_2$, by adding slaked lime, $Ca(OH)_2$, to seawater. $Mg(OH)_2$ is readily converted to magnesium oxide, MgO, which is used, for example, in refractory bricks to line steel furnaces. This application accounts for much of the industrial use of magnesium, so there is little need for the energy-intensive conversion to magnesium metal.

Where evaporation of seawater is locally greater than the inflow of fresh water from rivers, the dissolved elements become steadily more concentrated until the least-soluble salts reach saturation and are precipitated. Precipitation occurs *not* in order of the abundances of the dissolved minerals, but in the order of least solubility. The least-soluble salts precipitate first, in the sequence shown in Figure 5.1. The percentage figures show the amount of the original seawater left at the point when each salt starts to precipitate; the relative proportions of salts formed on total evaporation are indicated by the sizes of the triangles. The first compound to precipitate is calcium carbonate ($CaCO_3$). This is the only mineral that forms until evaporation has reduced the seawater to 19% of its original volume. This precipitate would form a limestone, such as the oolite described in Section 4.1.

When 81% of the seawater has evaporated, gypsum ($CaSO_4.2H_2O$,) begins to form. In the crystal structure of gypsum, two molecules of water are associated with one molecule of calcium sulphate. Only if evaporation continues to less than 9.5% of the original water volume is it joined by the next least soluble evaporite mineral, halite (NaCl), also known as common salt. But if evaporation proceeds beyond this point, huge quantities of NaCl can be obtained. The most soluble salts are the chlorides of potassium and magnesium; only when evaporation is almost complete are these salts thrown out of solution. In nature, complete evaporation of whole seas is very rare, and so these most soluble evaporite salts are rarely found preserved in sequences of sedimentary rocks.

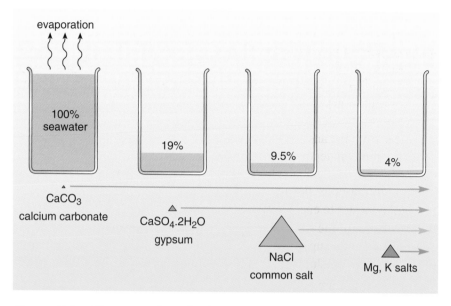

Figure 5.1 The succession of salts precipitated from seawater on evaporation. During evaporation of the first 81% of water, only calcium carbonate ($CaCO_3$) is formed. When evaporation has reduced the water volume to 19%, gypsum ($CaSO_4.2H_2O$) starts to precipitate. When only 9.5% of the original water is left, halite (NaCl) begins to precipitate, and magnesium and potassium salts begin to come out of solution at 4% of the original volume. The arrows indicate that the salts may continue precipitating throughout evaporation. The areas of the triangles indicate the relative proportions of the salts formed on complete evaporation (see fourth column of Table 5.1).

Question 5.1

Using the data in Table 5.1, estimate the thickness, in metres, of the evaporite minerals halite and gypsum that would be formed if a closed sea, 100 m deep, evaporated completely. Assume that each mineral has an average density of $2\,t\,m^{-3}$, and forms a single, distinct, separate layer (although in practice mixed layers would form).

It is clear from the answer to Question 5.1 that the formation of layered evaporite mineral deposits up to hundreds of metres thick would require evaporation of vast quantities of seawater. For such accumulations of evaporites, three conditions must be met:

- shallow water to enable efficient solar heating and fast evaporation;
- subsidence of the sea floor on which they are forming, otherwise the salts could only build up to sea-level;
- frequent replenishment of the saltwater to renew supplies of dissolved salts.

These conditions are provided by two different *natural* situations: **sabkhas** and **salinas**, both of which are areas of shallow or ephemeral water in hot climate zones (mainly within 35° of the Equator).

5.1.1 Modern evaporitic environments

Sabkhas

A sabkha is an area of low-lying, generally coastal mudflats where the area is periodically flooded, the water evaporates, and the area floods again to allow a mixed evaporite–clay zone to build up (Figure 5.2). Deposition of evaporite and associated carbonate minerals may be by direct precipitation at the surface (e.g. halite), or by crystallization from subsurface **brines**. Gypsum and anhydrite ($CaSO_4$) often form as nodular masses within the sediments. Many subsurface anhydrite deposits later hydrate to form exploitable gypsum deposits.

Figure 5.2 Block diagram illustrating the different sedimentary successions developed in a sabkha environment, including the sites of precipitation of the evaporite minerals gypsum, halite and anhydrite. More soluble salts (e.g. halite) are precipitated further inland from the lagoon. Anhydrite only occurs near the surface, whereas hydrated calcium sulphate (gypsum) forms in the sediments below the surface, in some cases due to the hydration of anhydrite by circulating groundwater.

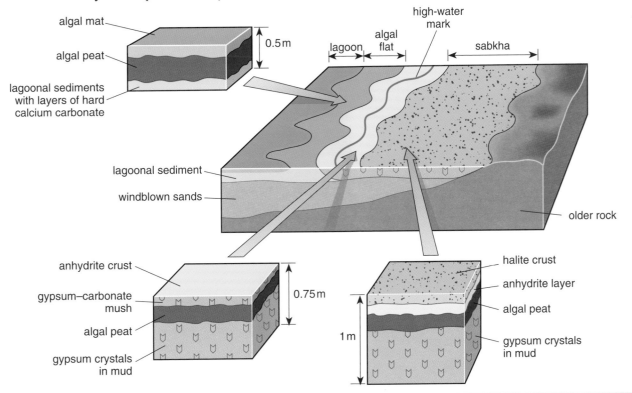

Salinas

Salinas, or salty lakes in arid climates, are also important sources of evaporites, particularly high-salinity brines. Often at high elevation, the water in these restricted basins is confined almost exclusively to the minimal rainfall within the basin catchment. If the catchment area geology involves weathering of rocks that liberate alkalis, they eventually end up in the basin as salts or high-strength brines within the groundwater or surface lakes (Figure 5.3). Dry areas of salt deposits, known as saltpans, are common in such climates. They occur on the margins of shrinking saline lakes or mark the site of a lake that has completely evaporated.

Artificial evaporite deposits

Several of the rarer evaporitic minerals (e.g. borates and lithium salts) are produced from the evaporation of concentrated brines (such as those in the inland lakes described above) in restricted, artificial ponds known as **solars** (Figure 5.4). A solar is simply the artificially created counterpart of a sabkha or salina, where a series of banked ponds is formed and periodically flooded with either seawater or brine. This water is then sealed in and allowed to evaporate until the contained salts are deposited. Such evaporating ponds are usually only effective in hot climatic zones, but even so, products of coastal solars represent an essentially renewable resource. Solars are common in areas of the Middle East, North Africa, South America and, on a spectacular scale, around the inland hypersaline Dead Sea.

Figure 5.3 Pink salt lake, South Australia. The salt deposits form a white fringe to the lake in the lower right of the photograph, where the vehicle tracks have broken through the salt crust. The pink colour is due mainly to salt-loving (halophilic) bacteria.

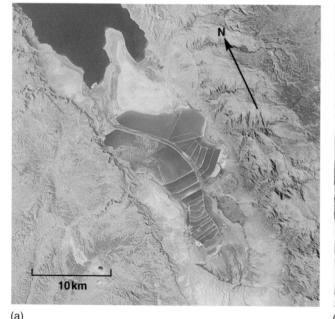

(a)

(b)

Figure 5.4 Two landsat images of the southern Dead Sea, showing increase in the development of solars in the southern lake from August 1989 (a) to March 2001 (b).

5.1.2   Evaporites in the geological record

Although in modern environments only relatively small quantities of evaporite minerals are being formed, the geological record contains evaporite mineral deposits which in total are tens or even hundreds of metres in thickness, as for example in the Permian strata (250 Ma) of northeast England and beneath the North Sea, and in Triassic rocks (200 Ma), which contain the famous Cheshire salt beds. There is much debate about the processes responsible for accumulating such thick salt deposits: theories range from deepwater basins with a deep saline layer, to shallow, evaporating semi-isolated basins with periodic recharge of brines by flooding — perhaps similar to embayments in the modern Caspian Sea.

Figure 5.5 shows the average composition of evaporite mineral sequences found in the geological record, and a blank row for use with Question 5.2.

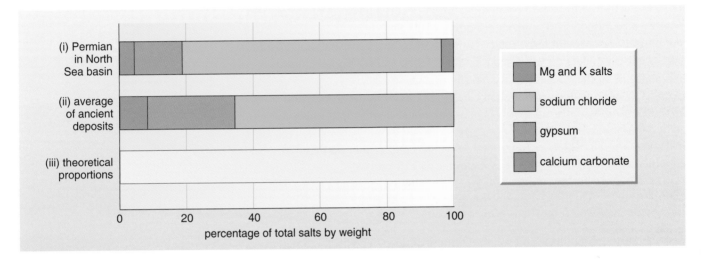

Question 5.2

Figure 5.5 shows the relative abundances of evaporites averaged for: (i) North Sea Permian sequences; (ii) all the world's evaporites throughout the geological record.

(a) Fill in row (iii) in Figure 5.5 to show the proportions of evaporite minerals which would be expected theoretically if complete evaporation of typical seawater occurred today (Hint: you need to refer back to Table 5.1).

(b) Which evaporite minerals are *more* abundant in evaporites found in nature (rows i and ii), compared with the theoretical abundance expected from complete seawater evaporation (row iii)? Why might this be so?

(c) Which evaporite minerals are *less* abundant in evaporites (rows i and ii), compared with the theoretical abundance (row iii)? Why might this be so?

Figure 5.5   Relative abundances of the major evaporite minerals: (i) averaged for Permian sequences beneath the North Sea; (ii) averaged for all evaporite sequences in the geological record; (iii) theoretical abundances for Question 5.2.

5.2   Halite: common salt

Halite is the mineral name for common salt (sodium chloride). Salt is essential for regulating bodily functions; the human body contains around 230 g of salt. Humankind's use of salt goes back at least 6000 years, and it has played an important role throughout that history, in politics, war and religion, as described earlier in Box 1.2.

5.2.1   Forms of deposit and extraction methods

The development of drilling technology prompted by exploration for salt in the 19th century was a major advance in the new science of geology. It also led to the search for, and exploitation of, the hitherto uninteresting, black tarry material we now know as oil, that is often found associated with salt deposits.

Salt deposits take a number of forms (Table 5.2). Subsurface deposits are exploited commercially on a large scale, and while sabkha and salina deposits are important salt resources, they are more important as sources of other evaporitic minerals. There is also the enormous 'liquid resource' of salt in seawater. Some countries produce drinking water by desalination of seawater and the salt is usually returned to the sea as high-strength brine. This could also be a source of salt in the future, if required.

Rock salt is mined from extensive, thick layers occurring within major ancient evaporite, carbonate and mudstone sequences (Figure 5.6a). The salt is drilled and blasted, or cut with large rotary cutters before being crushed and sized for sale. Some producers dissolve and recrystallize the salt for higher-quality applications. In the UK, salt beds are widespread in rocks of Upper Permian and Upper Triassic age and are mined in Cheshire both by underground and solution methods. **Solution mining** involves pumping water down pipes in boreholes drilled into the salt seams. The brine produced when the water dissolves the salt is then returned through an outer pipe to the surface. The brine is purified and may be evaporated in pans to produce granular salt products.

⬤   Which of the deposits in Table 5.2 are most likely to be worked on a large scale, and which by small-scale operations?

⚪   Underground mining and solution mining of deep deposits (sedimentary layers, domes or lake sediment evaporites) require considerable investment, and must be worked on a large scale to make a profit. By contrast, surface harvesting is usually a small-scale process (though some large-scale commercial operations are based on solars).

Table 5.2   Types of halite deposit.

Deposit	Example	Extraction method	Other evaporite minerals exploited
layers in marine sediments	Cheshire (UK)	underground mining; solution mining	potash, gypsum
diapiric domes*	Gulf Coast (America), Poland	underground mining; solution mining	gypsum
lake sediment deposits	California, Turkey, Wyoming	underground mining; solution mining	borates, soda ash
saltpans, saline lakes	Chile, East Africa	harvesting by hand	soda ash, borates, lithium salts
sabkhas	Arabian Gulf	harvesting by hand	
solars	Thailand, Philippines	harvesting by hand or machines	
seawater		(potential future source)	bromides, magnesium salts

* Diapiric domes are typically formed by balloon-shaped masses of low-density material (e.g. salt or granite) that rise gradually through denser rocks from depth, displacing the rocks above to form a domal structure at the surface.

Salt is also extracted from major diapiric domes (Figure 5.6b and c), either by underground mining or solution mining. Salt has an amazing ability to flow under pressure. At depth, layered salt deposits may flow towards zones of lower pressure, causing complex folding in the layers. In some areas, the salt flows upwards to form massive diapiric columns that may be 2.5 km in diameter and extend to depths of 7.5 km. Another resource associated with salt domes is sulphur (Section 7.2.3), which is sometimes found in the caprock sequence, while the deformed strata around the **diapirs** may form important traps for oil and gas. Salt's ability to flow means that any voids left after extraction are self-sealing and impermeable (provided some marginal salt remains to line the cavity). Old salt workings are therefore increasingly favoured for deposition or storage of a range of materials, including petroleum, radioactive waste and, possibly in the future, carbon dioxide, to reduce its release into the atmosphere and alleviate global warming.

Small-scale mining from saltpans and salt lakes occurs in many developing countries. This is often seasonal, with salt being deposited in the dry season as the saline lake waters evaporate. Solars are more widespread and concentrate seawater, lake brines, or deeper brines extracted by borehole from saline aquifers.

Figure 5.6 Salt production from different deposits.
(a) Underground mining of salt: Fairport Mine, USA. (b) Image from the Space Shuttle of salt domes (dark circular areas) on the Iranian Gulf Coast (field of view approximately 200 km). (c) Cross-section of a diapiric salt dome exploited by solution mining. (d) Vast solars in San Francisco Bay, California. The numerous tracks in the top two solars are made by mechanical harvesters; a strip of salt about 200 m wide remains to be harvested in the top pond. The two ponds to the left contain concentrated brine, which is crystallizing salt; the red colour is due to halophilic bacteria.

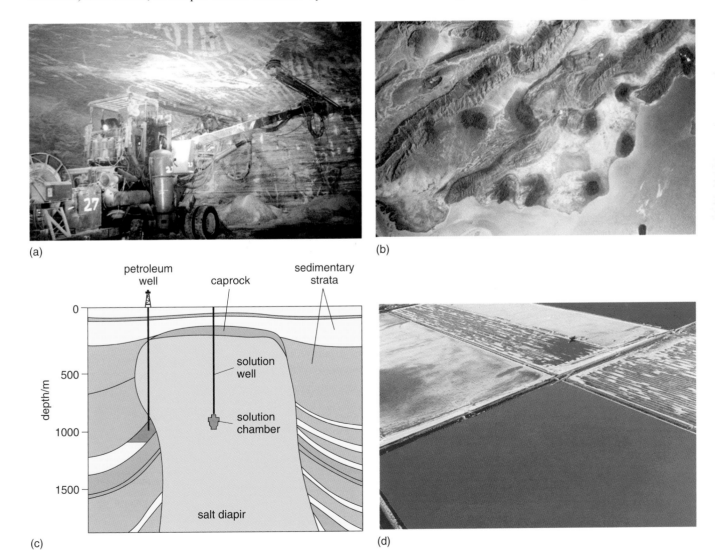

(a)

(b)

(c)

(d)

The brines are passed from pond to pond at increasing salinity. Salts are precipitated when they reach their respective saturation levels (Section 5.1). It takes 65 tonnes of seawater, and approximately 18 months, to make 1 tonne of salt. The crystallized salt is collected mechanically (Figure 5.6d) or by hand (Figure 1.4) from the dried-out ponds. The mixed salts can be used together for lower-grade applications or further processed for more specialized uses.

5.2.2 Global production and uses of salt

World salt production is around 225 million tonnes per year. Major salt-producing countries include USA, India, Mexico, the Netherlands, Poland, UK, Spain and Italy. Salt resources are immense and the marine resource alone makes it, for practical purposes, a limitless resource. Economic reserves are obviously less abundant but there is little immediate concern over long-term availability.

There are believed to be more than 14 000 uses of salt. Salt for culinary purposes accounts for only about 4% of world salt production. The main use of salt (> 65%) is as feedstock for numerous chemical processes that require Na or Cl, including the manufacture of chlorine, soda ash (Na_2CO_3) and hydrochloric acid. These chemicals are used in many manufacturing processes — for instance chlorine derivatives include PVC (polyvinyl chloride) plastic. Halite itself is also used as a food preservative, for seasoning, and in agriculture (e.g. salt licks for cattle, and in animal feed). It can act as a water softener, exchanging Na^+ ions for the Ca^{2+} and Mg^{2+} ions that cause hard water, thus preventing limescale build-up in pipes and appliances. Salt crystals are transparent to infrared radiation, and so find a use as lenses and prisms in specialized optical instruments, including some lasers. A major bulk use in cold climates is for road de-icing, though the increasing frequency of mild winters has had a major impact on rock salt production in the UK at least — a particularly direct case of the economic impact of global warming.

5.3 Other evaporites as industrial minerals

Apart from gypsum, which will be considered at the end of this chapter, three other evaporite minerals are exploited in significant amounts for industrial applications. These are potash, soda ash and borates.

5.3.1 Potash

Potash is the term used commercially to describe any of the potassium-bearing salts such as sylvite (KCl) and carnallite ($KMgCl_3.6H_2O$), or even brines that contain sufficient potassium to crystallize out as one of the potash salts. It is generally recovered from relatively deeply buried sedimentary evaporite deposits or from surface brines in lakes and inland seas. In the UK, potash is mined on the North Yorkshire coast at the Boulby Mine near Whitby, at the edge of the Permian sedimentary basin (known as the 'Zechstein' basin) whose deposits underlie much of central Europe and the North Sea.

● Most of the potassium salts occur at the margins of the Zechstein basin. Why should this be so?

○ Potassium salts are the most soluble evaporites, and thus require the most intense evaporation to be precipitated in large quantities. Evaporation would have been fiercest at the shallow margins of the Zechstein basin; the interior of the basin would have remained underwater and other, less-soluble evaporite minerals would have precipitated there.

At Boulby, seams of sylvite and halite approximately 7 m thick are mined now mainly offshore at depths of 1100–2000 m. The mine access tunnels are hewn from halite underlying the potash; this halite is sold as road de-icer. The mining is technically difficult due to the high temperatures at these depths (e.g. 42 °C at 1300 m depth), that make the evaporite rocks relatively weak and liable to deform slowly, closing in on shafts and tunnels that are not maintained.

Many of the world's biggest potash deposits are in Saskatchewan, Canada (Figure 5.7). The province is the world's largest exporter, supplying 25–30% of world demand at the turn of the 21st century. The potash layers are generally mined from depths of up to 1400 m. Careful construction of shafts through aquifers above the evaporite layers is needed to avoid water entering the mine. Where water *does* become a problem, or depth precludes economic extraction, solution mining is employed. Hot water is injected via boreholes drilled down into the potash, which is preferentially dissolved because sylvite dissolves more easily than halite at elevated temperatures. The potash-enriched saturated brine is returned to the surface via 'extraction wells' and then the soluble salts are purified and crystallized.

Potash is also obtained from surface brine sources. Natural potash-rich brines are allowed to evaporate in solars to produce a mixture of carnallite and halite. This mixture is processed to produce pure potash salts and a range of other by-products. The Dead Sea, Great Salt Lake and Qarhan Lake in China are important surface sources of potash brine.

Figure 5.7 Canadian evaporite deposits. (a) Sketch map showing the extent of evaporites (yellow) of the Elk Point–Broadview Syncline, a Silurian–Devonian evaporite basin. (b) Cross-section through the Broadview Syncline (location shown in (a)). Potash seams occur in the upper part of the evaporite sequence.

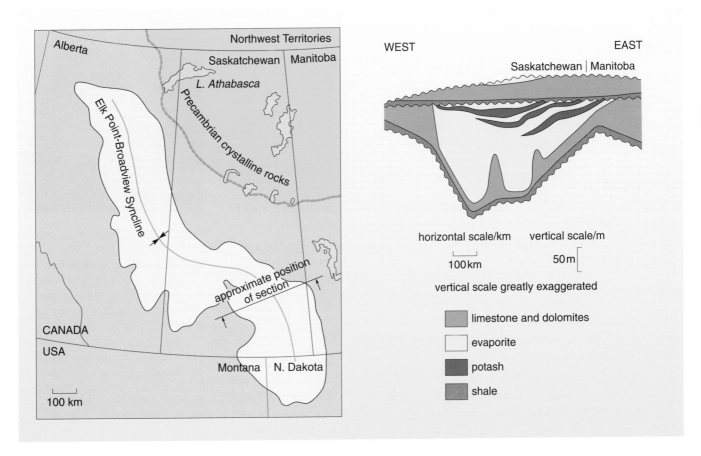

World production of potash was around 27 Mt in 2001, with Canada being the main producer, followed by Russia, Belarus, China and Chile. World resources of potash are regarded as immense: the US Geological Survey estimates 17 billion tonnes, of which 8.4 billion tonnes are considered exploitable. However, reserves are unevenly distributed, with ~75% in Canada and Russia. Its importance to the global fertilizer industry makes potash one of the world's major traded industrial mineral commodities: over 95% of potash production is consumed by agriculture. Typically combined in bulk with nitrogen and phosphorus compounds, it supplements depleted soils and boosts crop yields. The trend in potash consumption is increasingly away from the intensive agriculture of the industrialized world and towards the growing populations of the developing world, which now (in the early 2000s) consume over 50% of annual production.

Potash salts share some uses with common salt, such as water softening, road de-icing, and food additives. High-quality 'lead crystal' glass for tableware is made with a flux of potash (rather than soda ash), making it brighter and harder, and thus better for engraving. Soap was originally made (around 3000 BC) by mixing wood ash (potash) with fat in water — and the same basic ingredients are used today for liquid soaps. Potash is also used to make the potassium chemicals used in matches, fireworks and explosives. Concern over excessive salt (sodium chloride) in modern diets has led to the development of culinary salt products based largely on potassium chloride, so many of us now regularly eat potash salts at mealtimes.

5.3.2 Soda ash

Soda ash (Na_2CO_3) is one of the major raw materials on which a range of important industrial sectors rely, and has been exploited for over 5000 years. Soda ash usually forms in shallow alkaline lakes, and large deposits are rare. All known commercially significant deposits are of Tertiary age or younger. Soda ash forming today in shallow lakes within the African Rift Valley, for example Lake Magadi and Lake Natron (Figure 5.8), is derived from weathering of the surrounding volcanoes (some of which are carbonatites).

World soda ash production in 2002 (37 Mt) was dominated by the USA. The main sources are:

- the massive deposits of the Green River Formation worked by underground mining methods in Wyoming, and
- the sodium carbonate-rich brines from Searles Lake, a saltpan near Death Valley in the Mojave Desert, California.

As with many other resources in the early 21st century, competition from China is increasing yearly. Global reserves are enormous, with 30–50 billion tonnes of recoverable mineral in the Green River Basin alone.

Question 5.3

(a) About 15 Mt of soda ash are extracted from the Green River Basin deposits each year. What is the *minimum* lifetime of these reserves at current rates of extraction?

Figure 5.8 Image taken from the Space Shuttle of Lake Natron, East African Rift Valley, an alkaline lake where soda ash is being precipitated along with other salts (pale areas). The pink colour of the water is due to a 'bloom' of red halophilic bacteria that thrive in the salty water and, incidentally, impart a vivid pink colour to the flamingos which feed on them. The lake is about 56 km in length.

(b) Only 8.3 Mt of soda ash are actually produced each year from these deposits after processing of the raw material. What is the percentage wastage during processing?

Currently, soda ash is used mainly in the glass, chemical, detergent, and paper industries, with roughly half of it consumed by glass-making. Almost every window, bottle, jar or light bulb contains a significant proportion of soda ash, as it provides the main fluxing component required to manufacture soda-lime glass. This is used for most flat (window) glass, and container (bottle) glass, as well as more specialist applications, such as fibreglass. In detergents, soda ash both aids oil stain removal and acts as a water softener.

Soda ash itself is not recycled by industry, but the increased use of recycled glass — as secondary aggregate, and in abrasives, fluxes, fibreglass and decorative products as well as in glass-making — has reduced the level of demand for primary soda ash in the glass industry.

5.3.3 Borates

Though relatively uncommon, boron is an element that many of us use regularly, for instance in Pyrex® kitchenware and in laundry powder. It is almost solely extracted from evaporite deposits, usually alkali borates within saline–alkaline lake sediments (as in Turkey), or brines formed in arid terrains. Borate deposits originate when boron-rich fluids derived from volcanic rocks or spring waters drain into restricted basins that are subject to intense evaporation. On saturation, a range of sodium, calcium, magnesium and hydrous borate minerals are precipitated. To form sizeable deposits, these highly soluble minerals must also be preserved from redissolution, usually by deposition of intervening clay-rich sediments. Colemanite ($Ca_2B_6O_{11}.5H_2O$) and borax ($Na_2B_4O_7.10H_2O$) are examples of major commercial borates.

One large open pit, appropriately sited at Boron, California, accounts for almost half of the world's supply of refined borates (borax and boric acid). The extraction methods are typical of many large-scale surface mining operations, but acid dissolution techniques are also under development in the USA. Calcium borates are dissolved at depth in hydrochloric acid that is circulated down boreholes and reprecipitated using lime from the boric acid formed. Boron-rich brines are extracted from the deeper parts of the lake sediments at Searles Lake, California, where boron salts are also produced along with soda ash. Because 80% of world production of borates is produced by just two countries (the USA and Turkey), borates are widely traded.

Major users of borates are the glass, detergent, agricultural and ceramic glaze industries. Borate is an important component that fluxes, stabilizes and gives thermal shock resistance and flexibility to glass, including Pyrex® glass. Borosilicate glass is used to encase high-level nuclear waste; fibreglass is used for insulation. Boron is an important agricultural nutrient at trace element level, and is added to fertilizers to ensure optimum growth and yield, particularly for fruit and vegetables. It is also the main bleaching agent in most laundry powders and in many multi-purpose detergents.

Box 5.1   Three minor evaporite minerals: lithium, strontium and iodine salts

Table 5.3   Minor evaporite minerals.

Evaporite	Source	Production/t*
lithium salts	arid basin brines (Chile, USA, China)	15 100
celestite (SrSO$_4$)	sabkha deposits (Mexico, Spain, Turkey)	360 000
iodine salts	natural petroleum field brines (Japan, USA, China, Russia)	9 300
	caliche deposits (Chile)	11 400

* Production figures are global, for 2002.

The two largest lithium brine operations are in northern Chile at Salar de Atacama (Figure 5.9a), a high-altitude, low-rainfall basin with internal drainage and fierce evaporation. Dual input of lithium (Li) from geothermal fluids and weathering of the nearby Andes has led to brines with average lithium concentrations of 4000 mg l^{-1}. Before lithium was extracted from such brines, it was obtained from lithium-bearing minerals in pegmatites. Many pegmatite mines have now closed due to competition from cheap brines from saline lakes similar to the Salar de Uyuni (Figure 5.9b).

Lithium compounds are used in lightweight batteries, substituting for lead or cadmium, both of which are more toxic. Lithium metal is the lightest known metal, so it is used in strong, light alloys with aluminium, copper and manganese for aircraft components. Lithium acts as a strengthening agent in ceramics and glass (e.g. the mirrors used in large telescopes), and lithium carbonate is used in the treatment of mood disorders.

Celestite (strontium sulphate) was mined from 1880 to the mid-1990s in the UK near Bristol from nodular deposits in the Upper Triassic Mercia Mudstone.

About 75% of strontium compounds obtained from celestite are used in colour television tubes as shielding; another application includes making widely used ceramic ferrite magnets, which are cheap, stable and corrosion-resistant. Strontium compounds also produce the red colour in fireworks.

Iodine occurs in seawater at concentrations of about 0.05 mg l^{-1}, but is produced mainly from two terrestrial sources: brines associated with oil and gas fields (e.g. in Japan), and sedimentary deposits known as caliche in Chile. A minor competing source of iodine is as a by-product from the world's largest seaweed drying factory in Iceland. Some light-sensitive iodine compounds are used to make photographic film. Iodine is also used in a similar way to the 'barium meal' to highlight organs on an X-ray image. Tincture of iodine (a solution of iodine in alcohol) is used as a disinfectant. Another medical application is in the treatment of thyroid problems. A radioactive isotope of iodine can be targeted directly at the thyroid gland because it is the only organ in the body that concentrates iodine. The iodine then destroys the nodules causing the problem.

Figure 5.9   (a) White salt crusts forming at the edge of the Salar de Atacama, a salt playa in northern Chile where Li salts are worked.

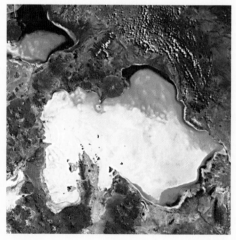

(b) Satellite image of the Salar de Uyuni, Bolivia, the largest salt playa (ephemeral lake) in the world (> 9000 km^2), taken in March 1973. Shallow briny water shows up blue, while uncovered saltpan is white. The saltpan contains lithium chloride (LiCl), as well as rock salt and gypsum, making this the biggest potential source of lithium in the world.

5.4 Gypsum: plaster for building

Gypsum ($CaSO_4.2H_2O$) is a form of calcium sulphate which usually occurs as layers or nodules in soft sediments that are thought to have formed in sabkha environments (Figure 5.10a). It is often found associated with the related but commercially undesirable mineral, anhydrite ($CaSO_4$), which generally underlies bedded gypsum deposits, and is also found with gypsum in the caprocks of salt domes (Figure 5.6c). Gypsum is a soft, white mineral, easily extracted either in open-cast excavations or in shallow mines. Most gypsum is extracted from bedded deposits, such as the Permian and Triassic successions of the UK.

Each year, large quantities of gypsum are produced worldwide: over 100 million tonnes in 2001, matched by a similar amount of synthetic gypsum recovered as a by-product of industrial processes (Figure 5.10b). Many large power stations use a 'scrubbing' system containing lime or limestone to remove sulphur from the exhaust gases before they are released to the air, according to Equation 5.1:

$$2CaCO_3 + 2SO_2 + O_2 + 4H_2O = 2CaSO_4.2H_2O + 2CO_2 \qquad (5.1)$$

limestone   flue gas   gypsum   carbon dioxide

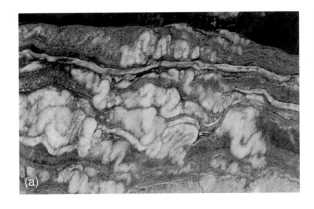

The UK produces large amounts of 'flue gas desulphurization' (FGD) gypsum due to the relatively high sulphur content of coals burnt at power stations. About 850 000 tonnes of synthetic gypsum were produced at two sites in the UK in 2002, and further FGD plants will be opened in the near future. In the UK, about 1.7 Mt are mined each year, while in 2002 a further 0.75 Mt were imported. Most mined and synthetic gypsum is used relatively locally, so that only about 20% is traded internationally.

The chief use for gypsum is in the manufacture of gypsum plaster and plasterboard, although it is also used as a component of cement to slow down the rate of setting. In the UK, a typical house has internal walls lined with plasterboard and covered with a thin layer (~ 3 mm) of gypsum plaster to give a smooth finish. Usually, ceilings consist of sheets of plasterboard (~ 8 mm) attached to the underside of the joists. This means that a typical three-bedroomed house can contain up to five tonnes of gypsum.

Equation 5.2 shows the first stage in the conversion of gypsum to plaster:

$$2CaSO_4.2H_2O \rightleftharpoons 2CaSO_4.^1/_2H_2O + 3H_2O \qquad (5.2)$$

gypsum   bassanite   water
                        (plaster of Paris)

Figure 5.10 Primary and secondary sources of gypsum. (a) Nodular veins of gypsum in Lower Cretaceous rocks, Dorset, UK (image approximately 0.5 m across). (b) Drax coal-fired power station, Yorkshire, UK. Secondary gypsum is a by-product of the process that removes SO_2 from the flue gases.

The forward reaction in Equation 5.2 is a dehydration reaction, in which heat expels three-quarters of the two molecules of the water from gypsum to form bassanite. Bassanite is the main constituent of plaster of Paris, made simply by heating gypsum to ~ 170 °C. When plaster of Paris is mixed with water at room temperature, rehydration occurs to produce gypsum (the reverse reaction in Equation 5.2). This is a good example of a reversible chemical reaction. Bassanite is the material used for soaking bandages to make casts for broken limbs and is the main component in making wall plaster and plasterboard. Plasterboard is made simply by sandwiching a core of plaster between two sheets of heavy paper.

- Gypsum is an important material for fire protection in buildings. Can you suggest why?

- Gypsum provides good fire resistance because the water held in the gypsum has to be 'boiled off' by the heat of the fire before the flame can break through the plasterboard.

Fire doors often incorporate a thick layer of gypsum plasterboard to protect this vulnerable point of a room. Similarly, a plasterboard ceiling provides a considerable check to the spread of fire, and firebreaks in lofts are often made of plasterboard. Plaster is also used in many non-construction areas including medicine, dentistry, sculpture and model-making. Even blackboard 'chalk' is not chalk ($CaCO_3$) at all, but mainly soft gypsum plaster!

Question 5.4

How does the reversible reaction in Equation 5.2 differ from the way water cements grains of sugar together as, in both cases, water seems to cause cementation?

Gypsum also has a large number of non-construction uses. It is used as a fertilizer (especially in mushroom farming), and as a soil conditioner — breaking down 'heavy' clay soils. Like calcium carbonate, it is added to foods such as flour and cereals to boost calcium levels. It is also used for hardening brewery water to produce paler, smoother beer. It is commonly used as filler in paints and paper. Among a host of other uses, it is employed by Hollywood to make fake 'movie snow'.

5.5   Summary of Chapter 5

1   Evaporites are a group of minerals precipitated when seawater or other brines evaporate in a restricted basin. They include alkali halides (e.g. NaCl), sulphates (e.g. gypsum) and borates.

2   Evaporite minerals are precipitated from seawater in order of increasing solubility: calcium carbonate, gypsum, halite, followed by the most soluble potassium and magnesium salts.

3   There are three main requirements for the formation of evaporite deposits: shallow water, basin subsidence, and periodic replenishment of seawater or brine. These conditions occur in two main natural environments: sabkhas and salinas.

4   Halite (common salt) occurs in a variety of geological deposits, including marine sediments, diapiric domes and lake beds. It is extracted mainly by underground mining or solution mining. Surface halite deposits include natural saltpans and salinas, sabkhas, and artificial ponds (solars), from which salt is often harvested on a small-scale by hand.

5   Among over 14 000 uses for halite, culinary salt is relatively minor, although vital. Salt is mainly used in the chemical industry, and in bulk for road de-icing.

6   Potash, soda ash and borates are three important evaporite minerals that are obtained mainly from inland saline lakes or buried lake deposits. Potash is used mainly in fertilizers, while soda ash and borates are both widely used in glass-making and detergents.

7   Lithium, strontium and iodine are produced from evaporite deposits or brines generally associated with restricted saline lakes.

8   Gypsum deposits form naturally in sabkha muds, but a secondary, synthetic source from desulphurization of power station flue gases is becoming increasingly significant.

9   Gypsum changes to plaster of Paris in a reversible chemical reaction involving the loss of water, and is widely used for the manufacture of plaster and plasterboard, so its chief bulk use is as a building material. It is also used in fertilizer, drilling muds, and as filler in paints and paper.

AGGREGATES: PAST AND PRESENT

6

6.1   Introduction to aggregates

Aggregates are granular materials used in construction, ranging in size from sand grains (for mortar) to large blocks weighing many tonnes (for sea defences). In many cases, a mixture of sizes is required.

Today there are three major sources of aggregates:

- sands and gravels (Section 6.2), many of which lie on top of solid rocks at the Earth's surface. Sand and gravel workings are mainly shallow pits on land or sub-marine dredge sites;

- crushed rock aggregates (Section 6.5) obtained by quarrying solid rocks that are then crushed and screened to give a range of particle sizes;

- manufactured and recycled aggregates (Section 7.2), which may be by-products of industrial processes (e.g. ash from coal-fired power stations, slag from steel-making), mine and quarry waste, or recycled construction materials (e.g. demolition waste, asphalt from roads). Although limited in application, usage of recycled materials will probably increase to reduce the demand for virgin resources — by the early 2000s, recycled aggregates were meeting 20–25% of the UK aggregate demand.

Sands and gravels, and crushed rock aggregates are often called 'natural' or 'primary' aggregates; 'secondary' aggregates are those that arise as waste during the extraction of other geological materials, such as coal, slate or china clay.

6.1.1   Aggregate sizes

Construction engineers and geologists may use different terms for different aggregate sizes (Figure 6.1), though there is broad agreement on what size of particles constitutes 'sand'. A geologist's silt and clay will tend to be called simply 'fines' by an engineer, whereas the term 'gravel' is much more common in the construction industry (for coarse aggregate) than in geology.

If a binding agent such as cement is to be used, aggregates usually exclude material larger than about 40 mm, but coarse aggregates sometimes use material up to about 75 mm. Pebbles coarser than 75 mm are either rejected or crushed before use. At the other end of the scale, 'fines' (clay- and silt-sized particles) can present a problem in aggregates used for concrete or asphalt because they tend to coat the larger particles and so stop the binding agent (cement for concrete; bitumen for asphalt) getting a good grip. Therefore 'muddy' aggregates must be washed to keep the fines below 10% (and in some cases, e.g. where concrete strength is crucial, below 3%) of the total weight. A sand and gravel deposit rich in fines is therefore much less desirable than one where natural processes have carried away all the fine sediment, leaving an aggregate ready for use. Sands are largely quartz. Gravel fragments of different rocks need a high crushing strength to make a good aggregate. Gravels containing fragments of weak rock (e.g. chalk) pose real problems for the engineer, because the aggregate may crumble under pressure.

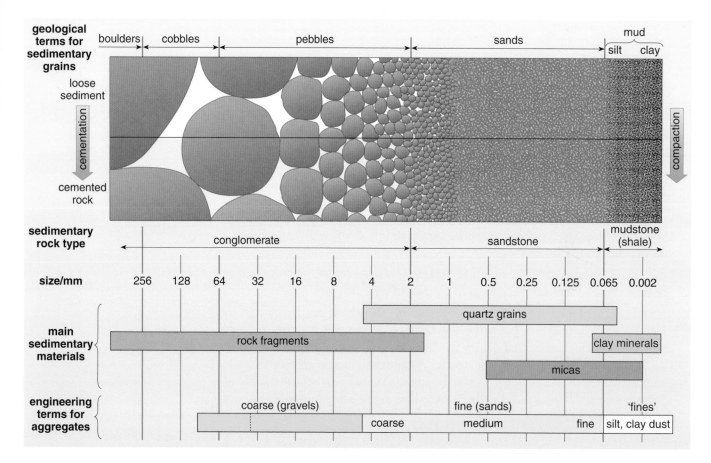

Huge amounts of unbound aggregates are used to make flat bases on which to lay new roads and the concrete floors of new buildings; this material is often termed **fill** (or 'hardcore').

● Why do you think that fines are avoided in aggregates used as fill (compare Figures 2.5a and b)?

◐ The 'fines' contain a lot of clay minerals that compact under pressure (Figure 2.5a) and may cause shrinkage as a clay-rich fill dries out. This is why holes dug in the road for drains etc. are usually filled with sand or gravel (before being covered with asphalt), which packs down to a stable mass with firm grain-to-grain contacts (Figure 2.5b), and is unlikely to settle further.

6.1.2   Growth of aggregate demand in the 20th century

Although 'ballast' was used in the 19th century to support railway tracks (Section 2.3.1), aggregates are largely a 20th-century phenomenon (Figure 6.2). The dramatic rise in aggregate production from 1920 to 1970 mirrors the demand for concrete and asphalt in construction, especially road-building, which is the principal consumer of aggregates in industrialized nations. Troughs on the graph are related to slow-downs in economic activity, which always have a dramatic effect on the construction industry.

Figure 6.1   Classification of loose sediment (top), and sedimentary rock (middle), by grain size. Silt is intermediate in grain size between sand and clay; the terms 'mud', 'mudstone' and 'shale' apply to mixtures of silts and clays. Of course, many sedimentary rocks contain mixtures of these grain sizes; for example, conglomerates are often 'pebbly sandstones'. The coloured boxes in the lower half of the figure show the size ranges of common sedimentary constituents. Engineering terms for aggregate particle sizes are given at the bottom of the diagram.

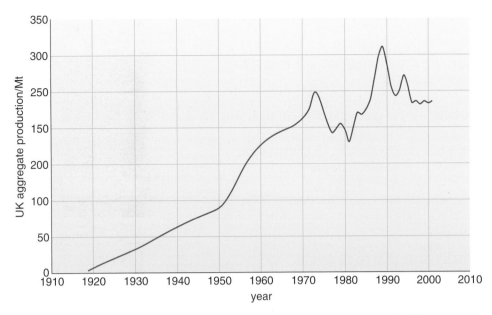

Figure 6.2 Growth of UK aggregate production in the 20th century.

The following may put the scale of aggregate production in more familiar terms.

● If all the aggregates consumed in the UK in 2000 ($\sim$ 220 Mt) came from a single vertical quarry face 25 m high by 100 m wide (about the size of the facade of Buckingham Palace), how far would this face need to be advanced in a year?

● Assuming a rock density of $2.5\,t\,m^{-3}$, an advance of 1 m would yield ($2500\,m^2 \times 1\,m \times 2.5\,t\,m^{-3}$) = 6250 t of rock per metre advanced. Thus the face would have to be advanced:

$$\frac{220 \times 10^6\ t}{6250\ t\ m^{-1}} = 35\,200 \text{ m, i.e. about 35 km each year.}$$

This equates to 96 m per day, representing a vast volume of quarried raw material. The sources of aggregate supply have changed markedly over recent decades (Figure 6.3).

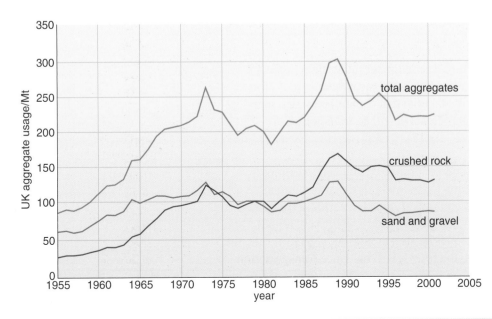

Figure 6.3 Amounts of sands and gravels, and crushed rock aggregates used in the UK between 1955 and 2001.

Question 6.1

Using Figure 6.3, compare sand and gravel production with that of crushed rock over each of the following periods: 1965–75, 1975–85, 1985–95, and 1995–2001.

Although the data from Figure 6.3 cannot be used to predict accurately what will happen in five years' time, the trend away from sands and gravels to crushed rock aggregates is clear. This trend is not confined to the UK; in France, sand and gravel production dropped from 72% to 53% of the aggregates market between 1970 and 1990.

6.2 Sands and gravels

6.2.1 Sands and gravel deposits and the rock cycle

Sands and gravels form as part of the 'drift', which is the unconsolidated material that has not been cemented or compacted to any degree, found draped over the solid bedrock (e.g. Figure 2.1). These **superficial deposits** are generally thin (up to 10 m), irregular layers and 'pockets', often present in river valleys.

What is the origin of sands and gravels? Weathering and erosion, especially of exposed rocks in highland areas, constantly provides fresh mineral grains (sand) and larger rock fragments (gravel), which are carried away by streams and rivers. Occasional severe storms can swell rivers to carry many times their 'normal' load of sediment, but sand and gravel are currently being extracted from working deposits in the UK much faster than they are being replenished by the rock cycle: they are not a renewable resource.

Deposition of sands and gravels

Transported sedimentary particles are laid down in layers as they reach quiet environments such as the sea floor or lakes. In time, the layers become consolidated to form fragmental or clastic sedimentary rocks, i.e. rocks made of fragments of pre-existing rocks.

● Would you expect to find deposits of fine-grained sediment in a fast-flowing stream or a slow-moving river?

○ A fast current will tend to carry along fine sediment rather than deposit it, leaving coarse-grained sand and gravel behind in the stream bed. A slow-moving river will deposit much finer material that cannot be carried in its weak current; only very fine clay particles will still be transported downstream.

Thus clay particles (Chapter 3), unlike coarser grains, can be carried along in suspension by sluggish currents, and deposited in low-energy environments (e.g. lakes). Coarser sediments such as sand and gravel are transported only by fast-flowing (high-energy) water. The individual grains tend to be broken, abraded and reduced in size as they roll or bounce along the stream bed. As a general rule, the further a sediment has been transported, the finer it will be, since transportation reduces the size of the particles.

● Why are large pebbles of soft rocks rarely found in river gravels?

◐ The high-energy environment needed to transport large pebbles would rapidly break down soft rocks during transport. Pebbles that survive river transport tend to be of hard crystalline rocks such as granites or quartzites, or of well-cemented sandstones and limestones, or of flint.

Sorting of sands and gravels

As sedimentary materials are transported and deposited, usually by water in the case of sands and gravels, there is a tendency for the particles to be sorted into different sizes. This degree of **sorting** depends mainly on how particles of different size and density settle through the current carrying them along (whether wind or water). The more uniform the conditions in the environment of deposition, the better sorted the sediment will be.

A well-sorted sediment contains grains of a similar size (Figure 6.4a), as might result from a long period of gentle washing back and forth of low-energy waves on a beach or desert sand blown by a steady wind. A poorly sorted sediment is one in which grains of various sizes are jumbled together (Figure 6.4b). This tends to happen when sediments have been deposited in variable conditions, for example in watercourses subject to drastic seasonal fluctuations in flow. Different degrees of sorting can be demonstrated by sieving sediments into different size fractions, and then plotting the mass of each size fraction as a **histogram**; the narrower the histogram, the better the sorting (compare Figure 6.4c and d).

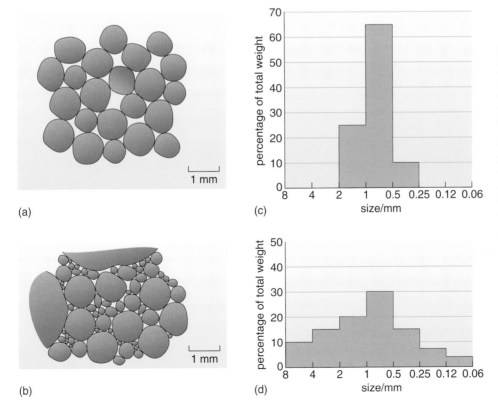

(a)

(c)

(b)

(d)

Figure 6.4   Well-sorted and poorly sorted sands: (a) sketch of well-sorted sand — most of the grains are of similar sizes, leaving a lot of pore space between the grains; (b) sketch of poorly sorted sand, where the mixture of grain sizes packs together better, reducing porosity; (c) histogram of the well-sorted sand (narrow, with high peak); (d) histogram of the poorly sorted sand (broad, low peak). (When plotting sediment sizes, by convention, histograms are drawn as here, with the coarsest grain size shown on the *left*, and with the grain size halving at each division to the right on the horizontal axis. This corresponds to the sequence of sizes passing down a normal stack of sieves.)

The size distribution of many industrial granular materials is also commonly plotted as a histogram to emphasize different degrees of sorting, which often influence the material's properties. For example, the predominant grain size of a sample is easy to see from the position of the 'peak' of the histogram.

An important note on 'sorting' of natural sediments and aggregates

Engineers describe a good aggregate as a **well-graded material**: one that contains a wide variety of grain sizes, and so compacts down to make a stable, dense, low-porosity material. Such a material found in nature *would be called 'poorly sorted' by a geologist*. So the term 'sorting' is sometimes used *in engineering in exactly the opposite sense to the geological one*. For the engineer, a poorly graded or poorly sorted aggregate is one with fragments all of the same size, which will form a weaker, porous aggregate, full of spaces.

Well-graded aggregates are generally preferred in construction, as they compact well to a bulk material with low porosity, which is likely to be stronger and less prone to frost damage (Section 2.1.2).

- Will perfect spheres have a higher or lower porosity than irregular fragments of similar size?

- They will have a higher porosity, whereas irregular fragments will tend to fit together better than perfect spheres, and so have a *lower* porosity.

- Will a rock with a range of grain sizes have a lower or higher porosity than one with a single grain size?

- A mixture of grain sizes will fit together better than grains of a single size, just as in a well-graded aggregate. Smaller grains can fit between the larger ones, so a rock with a variety of grain sizes will have a lower porosity than one with a single grain size (compare Figures 6.4a and 6.4b).

6.2.2   Distribution of sands and gravels in the UK

Large deposits of coarse, pebbly material are found not only along rivers in the UK, but also as 'sheets' or terraces far up on the valley sides. This implies that, in the past, more coarse sediment was supplied to larger, more vigorous rivers than those present in the UK today. Similar coarse deposits occur today at the margins of the Himalayan mountains, where turbulent rivers emerge onto the plains and spread into vast, braided channels. However, when these coarse sediments were laid down in Britain there were no high mountains nearby to supply this sand and gravel, so we must seek another modern analogy. The margins of glaciated regions such as Greenland also feature vast, braided rivers carrying huge loads of coarse sediment.

The Quaternary ice age in Britain

Alternating warm and cold climatic episodes during the Pleistocene meant that much of Britain was repeatedly covered by ice sheets, some of which were several kilometres thick. During one cold period, the ground was permanently frozen (permafrost) almost to Spain, and so much water was locked up in ice sheets that sea-level was 120 m lower than it is today (Figure 6.5). In warmer times, about 120 000 years ago, hippopotamuses are known to have roamed as far north as Leeds. Meltwater from the ice-sheet margins formed large, vigorous rivers that deposited coarse sands and gravels, predominately in the summer after each spring thaw. Each time the climate warmed up and an ice sheet melted rapidly, all the material still held in the ice, from boulders to finely ground 'rock flour', was left behind as a poorly sorted mass of sediment (known as **till** or boulder clay) that blankets much of Britain today. The wide range of grain sizes and high proportion of fines prevents till being an important aggregate resource.

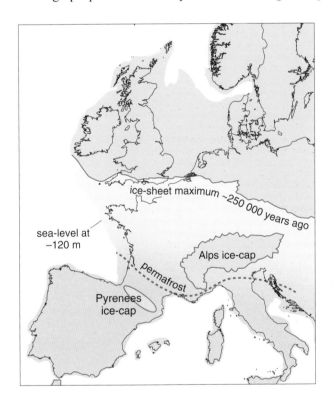

Figure 6.5 Maximum extent of the ice-caps and frozen ground in Northern Europe about 250 000 years ago, when the sea (unshaded area) was 120 m below its present-day level.

Most of the important sand and gravel deposits in the UK originate at least in part from increased upland erosion in glacial periods due to freeze–thaw and the grinding action of glaciers. It has been estimated that moving ice can erode the rock surfaces underneath by as much as 1 mm per year. Large masses of sediment that accumulated near the edge of the melting ice sheets were further transported and sorted ('reworked') by rivers during warmer episodes, spreading sheets of sand and gravel across the major valleys and lowlands. As the last ice melted and sea-level rose, some of these lowland deposits became submerged (Section 6.3.2). Reworking often improves sorting, as fines tend to be carried further downstream, leaving a coarser-grained, better-sorted deposit that is more valuable as an aggregate. Figure 6.6 shows the location of important commercial UK sand and gravel deposits, many of which are reworked glacial material.

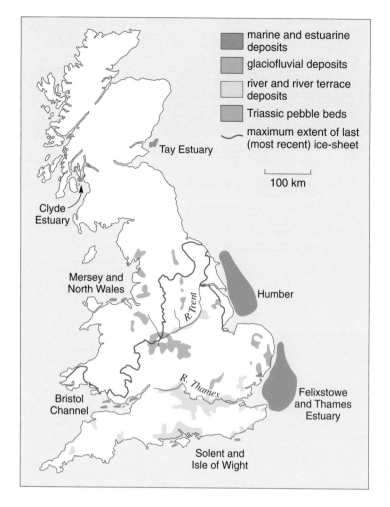

Figure 6.6 Major areas where onland and offshore sands and gravels have been worked in the UK; glaciofluvial deposits were formed by streams flowing from the melting ice.

It is clear from Figure 6.6 that many of the sand and gravel deposits worked today are in central and southern Britain towards the edge of the ice, or just outside the ice sheet. Why do you think this is so?

There are two reasons. Firstly, the ice sheet carried loose surface soil, sand and gravel to its margins, where melting ice deposited unsorted till that was then reworked by meltwater into sand and gravel deposits. Secondly, this area has the highest population density, so local *demand* for aggregates is highest.

6.3   Sand and gravel extraction

6.3.1   River terrace sands and gravels

River terrace deposits tend to occur as more or less irregular strips of sand and gravel at definite heights along the sides of major river valleys, corresponding to previous river flood plain levels. The oldest terrace is the highest; the youngest occupies the present flood plain of the river. A typical section across the Thames in central London is shown in Figure 6.7. Two older terraces lie well above the present flood plain. Sand and gravel can be worked in all these terraces, but pits in the upper terraces are less liable to flood after extraction. Any excavations

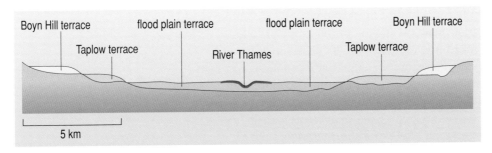

Figure 6.7 River valley terrace deposits in the Thames valley. The oldest deposits are on the top terraces; each lower terrace marks a later stage when erosion of the river had cut the valley deeper. The most recent gravels are those of the present flood plain on the valley floor.

below the present river level will flood because they are below the **water table** (the level in the ground below which the rocks are saturated with water).

Terrace and flood plain deposits provide good-quality aggregates because the rivers that deposited them have carried away most of the detrimental 'fines'. Fortunately, many large urban areas in the UK are in major river valleys containing large deposits of sand and gravel, such as the Thames and its tributaries around London. Some of the best river terrace deposits lie in the Heathrow area; lakes and reservoirs mark the locations of some workings, but huge reserves of sand and gravel have been covered up ('sterilized') by the building of the airport (Figure 6.8).

River terrace aggregates are dug out of open pits by mechanical diggers. They are then:

- washed to remove fines;
- sieved, to screen out large pebbles and sort the sediment into different grain sizes.

Figure 6.8 Gravel deposits in and around London. The Thames and most of its major tributaries have workable sand and gravel deposits.

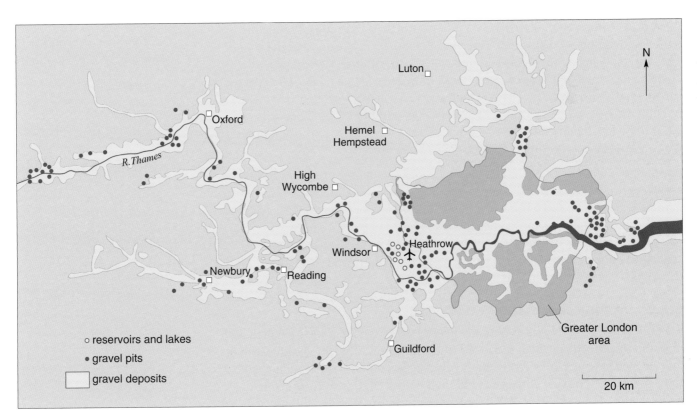

There is always some **overburden** of topsoil, subsoil or river mud and silt that is too fine grained for use, and has to be stripped off the top of the gravel. Modern workings (e.g. Figure 6.9) store the overburden in **bunds**, which are linear banks that screen the works; they may be used to restore the site after extraction. For a deposit to be economic, the overburden should be relatively thin (no more than a few metres thick), and *not more than one-third* of the thickness of the workable sand and gravel. This is often expressed as the **overburden ratio** (overburden : workable deposit thickness) that, for low-value materials such as sands and gravels to be viable, should be less than 1 : 3.

Figure 6.9 A working gravel pit in Northamptonshire. The shallow excavations where extraction takes place lie between the trees in the background and the conveyor belts and screening plant (left of centre). Stockpiles of sand and gravel graded into different sizes can be seen, along with a grassed-over bund (screening bank) on the left of the photograph.

When higher-value resources such as limestone (Chapter 4) or coal are extracted from open pits, the overburden ratio can be much higher (ratios of between 5:1 and 30:1 are not uncommon).

Like all sediments, sands and gravels tend to occur in layers. Marine sediments often occur as layers of almost constant thickness over large areas, reflecting the uniform conditions of deposition. However, conditions in streams and rivers are very different, changing rapidly and frequently with variations in season and climate, and individual deposits are often confined to a single valley. Hence most fluvial sand and gravel deposits are small and very variable, often occurring as roughly lens-shaped bodies along the valley sides and floor. These deposits are generally a few hundred metres to a few kilometres in length, tens of metres wide, and a few metres thick.

Assessing the economic potential of a sand and gravel deposit requires a detailed knowledge of the volume and composition of the deposit before work begins. The normal method is to drill a pattern of boreholes, from which the thickness of both the overburden and the deposit can be worked out, and to take samples for particle size analysis by sieving. Detailed borehole data can be used to plot sophisticated contour maps or 3-D images of a rock or ore body, but these techniques are rarely applied to low-value resources such as sand and gravel.

6.3.2 Marine sands and gravels

These deposits were originally laid down by ancient rivers that were swollen with meltwater at the end of the last ice age when sea-levels where much lower than today. Once submerged by rising sea-levels, the currents and tides winnowed out finer sediment to leave well-sorted sands and gravels that are well suited to aggregate production. Several of these sheets of sand and gravel around British coasts (Figure 6.6) are exploited today by sub-marine dredging. Marine aggregates must be well washed to remove salt, especially if they are for use in concrete.

As early as the 1550s, marine sands and gravels were extracted from the Thames estuary. At the turn of the 21st century, they are a useful supplement to land-based aggregates, resulting in fewer quarries and reduced road traffic. They are cheap to extract by dredging and large quantities can be readily transported by sea to distant markets. Up until the 1960s, less than 3 million tonnes of sand and gravel a year were produced from the sea around Britain, but this rose to about 28 million tonnes by the late 1980s, stabilizing at around 23 million tonnes by the early 2000s. At approximately 20% of the total sand and gravel output of the UK, this is roughly equivalent to the output of 50 inland quarries. However, in the long term it is likely that concerns about the possible effects on both marine life and coastal erosion of dredging huge tonnages of sea-floor sediment will limit the growth of this industry.

6.3.3 Sands and gravels from bedrock deposits

Some sand and gravel deposits laid down and buried well before the Pleistocene have remained more or less uncemented for hundreds of millions of years, and so can be easily worked in the same way as superficial deposits. The Triassic sandy pebble beds of the Midlands (Figure 6.6) are an example. In Durham, several quarries extract uncemented Permian (~ 280 Ma) desert dune sands at the same time as an overlying, well-cemented limestone for use as aggregate (Figure 6.10). Dominated by uniform (0.5–1 mm diameter), well-rounded quartz grains, the sands can be sold as building sand after simple screening.

Figure 6.10 Aerial view of a dual-product aggregate quarry in County Durham. Permian dune sands form the beige floor of the excavation, while the pale Magnesian Limestone worked for roadstone can be seen in steep faces at the top of the quarry. The two rock types are separated by a thin band of dark-grey shale that forms the dark ground near the quarry buildings.

⬤ Since these sands were laid down in a desert, would you expect them to be well sorted or poorly sorted, and of high or low porosity?

○ Desert dune sands are usually well sorted (the wind blows the fines away, leaving grains all of a similar size). This sand will have a high porosity (Figure 6.4a).

6.4 Planning and the environment

Many of the best deposits of superficial sands and gravels lie in the lower reaches of the main rivers of lowland Britain, the very places where population pressure puts most demand on the land for building, agriculture or recreation. Many good sand and gravel deposits cannot be worked as a consequence of this competition for space: in the London area alone as much as one billion tonnes of sand and gravel have been covered by built-up areas. When planning new urban developments, extracting sands and gravels *before* building begins or leaving the best sites for future exploitation is clearly the preferred course of action.

Abandoned sand and gravel pits on flood plains inevitably fill with water. In many cases, these lakes are given a new lease of life as wildlife sanctuaries or for angling or water sports, as a part of the restoration programme. An example of this is the Lower Farm Pit near Newbury (Figure 6.11).

Dry gravel pits can be restored to agricultural use by returning the soil and landscaping. In some cases, dry pits can be used for tipping wastes, provided that measures are taken to prevent contamination of the groundwater if the ground below is permeable (see Box 3.3).

In the 1980s, an escalation in demand for aggregate prompted fears of a crisis of aggregate supply in southeast England because the rate of sand and gravel extraction vastly exceeded the rate at which new planning permissions were being granted for future gravel workings. Reserves that aggregate companies have proved to be economic and have planning permission to extract are often called the **land bank**. Traditional 10-year land banks favoured by both local planners and extractors for long-term planning were reduced to 7 years in the 1990s as demand levelled off and other supplies (marine sand and gravel, crushed rock, and recycled materials) rose. We shall return to the issue of future aggregate supplies in Chapter 7.

Figure 6.11 Restored sand and gravel pit, Thames Valley near Newbury, Berkshire. The old flooded workings are now used for recreation.

Box 6.1 Specialist sands

Silica sands dominate the specialist sand industry. They are the main ingredient in glass, but their applications range from oil reservoir exploitation to bunker sand for golf courses.

Occurrence and extraction

Because quartz is a hard mineral with poor cleavage, chemically stable, and abundant in crustal rocks, it comes as no surprise that most sands contain an abundance of quartz. However, as the sorting process is never perfect, most sands are a mixture of rock fragments and minerals derived from the rocks that are weathering in the 'source area'. Provided all the grains are mechanically strong and stable, even impure sand should be suitable for construction. Specialist sand uses, however, demand a much purer material that is rich in quartz (SiO_2 >95%), with few impurities. Suitable sands are found only where unusually persistent geological processes have led to highly effective sorting, leaving a sand dominated by quartz. Most silica sands are extracted from poorly consolidated deposits or weakly cemented sandstones, but silica sand may also be produced from very pure quartzites.

In the UK, specialist silica sands are extracted mainly from Pleistocene sands in Cheshire; Cretaceous strata in Norfolk, Surrey, Kent, Bedfordshire and NW Scotland; and Carboniferous sands in Staffordshire and Fife (Figure 6.12). Despite its higher value, silica sand in the UK is still extracted from open pits, with the exception of the Loch Aline deposit in NW Scotland where a high-purity Cretaceous sandstone is mined underground. Worldwide, large reserves and resources exist but those worked are largely a function of market proximity. It is possible to consider these deposits as, to some extent, renewable as the creation and deposition of silica sand continues in beaches and desert environments at present.

To meet stringent specifications, the sands usually require extensive physical and sometimes chemical processing to clean the grain surfaces, remove impurities and produce the desired particle size distribution.

Uses and products

Most glasses are based on silica, so everyday items such as bottles, windows, light bulbs and TV screens are all made from silica sand. Typical glass contains 50%–70% silica sand. Silica sands ground to a fine flour are used as filler in rubber, sealants, paints, and plastics because their hardness improves the product's resistance to abrasion and chemical attack.

Since silica's melting point (1610 °C) is higher than that of iron, copper and aluminium, silica sand bound with some clay or resin makes strong foundry moulds for casting metal. A few sands from deposits (e.g. some beaches) dominated by dense, refractory minerals such as zircon, olivine, staurolite and chromite may be used in specialist foundry applications.

An application that demands very uniform grain size and clean, strong sand is in hydraulic fracturing of oil reservoir rocks near oil wells, or 'reservoir stimulation'. A sand–gel mixture is pumped down under pressure, opening up fractures in the rock. These fractures are then 'propped open' by the mass of sand grains. The fractures enhance the flow of oil to the well, increasing oil recovery. Sands used for this purpose are sometimes called 'proppants'.

International trade in silica sand is limited due to its relatively low value and wide availability. However, small quantities of specialist grades are moved worldwide, for example the 'standard' sands supplied for testing the abrasion resistance of rocks (Section 6.6.4) are sent from Leighton Buzzard in Bedfordshire to the Middle East: a true case of selling sand to the Arabs!

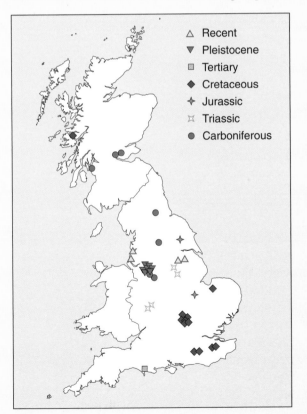

Figure 6.12 Locations of specialist sand quarries in the UK.

6.5   Crushed rock aggregates

The ease and thus low cost of extracting sands and gravels from mainly superficial deposits has made them the traditional source of aggregates for building in many regions.

○   What is the principal source of aggregate used in the UK today: sand and gravel, recycled wastes or crushed rock (Section 6.1)? Is there any recent trend in aggregate consumption?

○   Before the 1970s, sand and gravel dominated the supply, but since then crushed rock usage has increased at the expense of sand and gravel (Figure 6.3). Use of recycled wastes has also increased since the 1980s, but they still account for only a small percentage of the total aggregate supply.

For many modern construction projects, especially roads and high-strength concretes, crushed rock aggregate is a more suitable material than sand and gravel. There are other specialized applications, such as ballast used below railway tracks, where high crushing strength is needed. In these situations, crushed rock aggregates have always been preferred. Most railway ballast in the UK is made from igneous or metamorphic rock. However, the market for railway ballast in the early 2000s has steadied to a modest 2–3 million tonnes a year.

Conditions for establishing a quarry to produce crushed rock aggregate include:

- The rock must be strong to take high loads, and of low porosity so it is not easily damaged by frost.
- The site should contain a large quantity of rock with consistent physical properties.
- The rock should be readily accessible beneath a shallow overburden.
- The site should be suitable for quarrying, crushing and transporting the stone, ideally without flooding.
- The site should not pose a nuisance either to local residents or to visitors (e.g. people visiting scenic areas), but should be close to markets to minimize transport costs.

Sedimentary rocks as aggregates

To be suitable for use as crushed rock aggregate, a sedimentary rock must be well cemented to ensure strength and low porosity, with thick, horizontal or gently dipping beds that are easily accessible. The sedimentary rocks that best fit these criteria are the better-cemented sandstones and limestones, which tend to be older than Permian (>290 Ma in age). Most Carboniferous and older rocks occur to the north and west of a line drawn from Torquay to Hull, especially in Devon and Cornwall, South Wales, the Pennines and the central valley of Scotland. By far the most widely quarried rock is the Carboniferous limestone because it has low porosity, is strong and uniform in its properties, and is widely available in thick beds close to urban centres. Some Carboniferous sandstones are also used for aggregate, but generally most UK sandstones are too porous and poorly cemented, and thus liable to frost damage (Section 2.1.2). Some Jurassic limestones are used as aggregate, but tend to be thinner, more porous, and much softer than the Carboniferous ones.

Igneous and metamorphic rocks as aggregates

Many crystalline rocks make excellent aggregates because they are tough materials with strong interlocking textures and very low porosity (see Figure 2.2). Most igneous rocks make good aggregates, but many metamorphic rocks (e.g. slates, schists) have a strong preferred alignment of minerals, causing them to split into long, platy fragments that will not compact easily into a low-porosity aggregate. Some crystalline rocks contain very large crystals, such as the pink feldspars in the granite in Figure 2.2a. If these crystals have well-developed cleavage planes (e.g. feldspar or mica), then their tendency to split along those planes will weaken the aggregate fragments.

In the UK, most igneous and metamorphic rocks occur in the west and north, far from the main aggregate market in southeast England. They must be transported over long distances by rail or sea to meet the demand for high-quality aggregates in the southeast.

6.5.1 Extraction of aggregate

The rock is blasted from the quarry face with high explosives and crushed before being screened to final sizes. Crushed rock quarries are much larger than building stone quarries (Section 2.3.3) because a high output of aggregate is needed to make the operation economic, and this demands considerable capital investment. Some hard-rock aggregate quarries are very big indeed, with outputs of several million tonnes a year. What with blasting, crushing and screening to the required sizes, not to mention vehicles shovelling, hauling and dumping the rock around (and away from) the quarry, the impact of crushed rock extraction on its surroundings can be considerable. Dust, noise and other problems associated with building stone quarries are magnified many times in a typical crushed rock quarry. Crushed rock aggregate quarries are also subject to more stringent planning permission and working conditions than sand and gravel pits because they tend to be noisier and dustier. Table 6.1 summarizes the effects that quarrying may have on the environment.

Table 6.1 Environmental impacts of quarrying and stone extraction.

Environmental issue	Description	Solutions
visual impact	proposed size of quarry, spoil tips, plant, buildings	screening by banks (bunds) of waste or overburden; design of working faces
noise	health hazard or nuisance from blasting, processing plant and associated traffic	machinery development and sound-proofing of operations; screening by bunds, trees
dust	from drilling, blasting, processing, dumping, traffic	water sprays; enclosure of equipment; plant design; maintenance of roadways
blasting	ground vibration and air blast in surrounding area	controlling various blast parameters (e.g. explosive charge), avoiding adverse weather conditions
reclamation	restoration or modification of abandoned workings	landscaping; nature conservation; waste disposal; recreation; development
subsidence	in underground workings	design of original mine; infilling
chemical pollution	minimal: due mainly to machinery and traffic; fines in water courses	maintenance of machinery; minimization of traffic; enclosure of buildings and screening

6.6   Uses and production of aggregates

6.6.1   Uses of aggregates

Aggregates are not only important end products in themselves, but also the raw material for manufacturing other construction products, such as concrete, asphalt, and mortar. Around 200 million tonnes of aggregates are used annually in the UK, which averages out at about 4 tonnes per person. Of this, around 90% of all aggregates are used in construction. The main uses are for:

- *roads*: the UK network handles about 94% of passenger travel and more than 60% of freight. Aggregates are used at all stages of road construction, from the load-bearing base to the high-friction surface (Section 6.6.3);
- *railways*: some 2–3 million tonnes of aggregates are needed for track ballast each year;
- *housing*: construction of an average house, from the foundations to the roof tiles, uses around 50 tonnes of aggregates;
- *other buildings and structures*: footings/hardcore, mortar, multi-storey car parks.
- the *water industry*: aggregates are used in building and maintaining reservoirs and in sewage treatment works.
- *anti-erosion measures*: blocks for sea defences (armourstone), coarse aggregate for stabilizing embankments ('rip-rap').

Table 6.2 gives typical amounts of aggregate used in different types of construction. As a general rule, UK aggregate usage can be apportioned as one-third to roads; one-third to houses, offices and shops; and one-third to industrial and public works.

Table 6.2   Approximate amounts of aggregate for individual construction purposes.

Construction	Aggregate needed
1 m^3 concrete	2 t
3-bedroomed detached house	50 t
multi-storey car park	17 000 t
15-storey office block	50 000 t
major road	7 500 t km^{-1}
new railway line (French TGV)	15 000 t km^{-1}
new motorway, or airport runway	100 000 t km^{-1}
Channel Tunnel lining	1.5 million t

Question 6.2

What reasons could account for the move away from traditional sand and gravel resources towards crushed rock aggregates in recent years (Figure 6.3)?

In 2000, it was estimated that total aggregate production within the European Union was 2.6 billion tonnes, compared with 1.1 billion tonnes in the USA. Most European countries are self-sufficient in aggregate materials. However, while countries such as the UK contain ample resources of sand and gravel and crushed rock, others are deficient in one or the other. For example, the Netherlands lacks resources suitable for crushed rock aggregates, while Austria, landlocked and mountainous, is a net importer of sand and gravel. However, the low cost of aggregates makes them sensitive to transport costs, and they may be sourced more cheaply via a short cross-border route than a long distance within national borders.

European countries generally use aggregates roughly in proportion to the size of their economies. In 2000, Germany dominated European consumption of aggregate materials at around 487 million tonnes, or 19% of total EU consumption, partly due to rebuilding in the former East Germany. An interesting way of comparing consumption between countries is on a per capita basis (Table 6.3). Average consumption for the European community was around 6.8 tonnes per person, compared to 4.1 in the USA.

These figures may seem surprising, but because of the wide range of national populations, a large-scale engineering project in a small population country can greatly increase per capita consumption in the short term. Consider the construction of a new motorway in Belgium, where total aggregate consumption in 2000 was only 48 Mt.

Table 6.3 Aggregate consumption per capita in selected countries.

Country	Aggregate consumption/ t per capita
UK	4.0
Germany	5.9
France	6.7
Portugal	7.0
Spain	9.8
Ireland	10.0
Denmark	10.9
Finland	15.7

● What would be the percentage increase in per capita consumption if 100 km of motorway were built in Belgium in one year (in addition to the 'typical' aggregate consumption for 2000)?

○ 100 km of motorway needs 100 000 tonnes per km, i.e. 10 million tonnes in total. This represents a percentage increase in the total aggregate consumption of:

$$\frac{10\ \text{Mt}}{48\ \text{Mt}} \times 100\% = 21\%$$

The per capita increase is therefore also 21%.

6.6.2 Aggregates for concrete

It is only largely since 1920 that concrete has overturned the dominance of stone and brick for use in construction, while concrete reinforced with steel rods has become common even more recently, replacing steel girders in many structures. Reinforced concrete can resist the pulling forces that cause *tensile stresses* in structures, allowing it to be used in different ways from all the materials discussed so far in this book. For instance, concrete beams reinforced with steel can span great distances whereas brick or stone arches would require several pillars to cover the same distance. Moreover, a bridge of steel or reinforced concrete can sustain heavy loads using much less material than a brick or natural stone bridge. The two latter materials are strong in compression but very weak in tension, which is why you seldom see a load-bearing stone lintel much longer than a metre.

Concrete should be a hard, stable material that develops a high strength as the cement sets. This is best achieved by coating all the aggregate particles with cement, leaving as little pore space as possible between the fragments. Since much of the water added to concrete forms small pores, the least amount of water possible is used in order to maximize the final strength.

Most rocks with a high crushing strength will make good aggregate, but the strongest concrete is made with material that meets the following requirements:

1   *Shape*: fragments should be more or less equal in size in all directions, but still irregular in shape, rather than flat, spherical or elongated. Crushed slate makes a particularly poor aggregate, difficult to compact, and thus with high porosity.

2   *Size*: in general, coarse aggregates (above 40 mm) are used only when large masses of concrete (> 1 m thick) are being cast; if there are large aggregate fragments in concrete under 1 m thick, some air pockets may not be eliminated.

3   *Grading*: a mixture of particle sizes is vital so that smaller grains fill up the spaces between the larger ones, leaving as little pore space as possible. This also ensures maximum aggregate-to-aggregate contacts, which give the concrete its strength (Figure 6.4a and b). An ideal aggregate has a broad grain-size histogram with a low peak (Figure 6.4d).

Concrete aggregates are specified by defining a **grading envelope** within which all the aggregate particles should fall (Figure 6.13). Aggregates are tested by sieving a sample into different size fractions and then plotting the weight of each size fraction on a graph to check that the results fall within the specified limits.

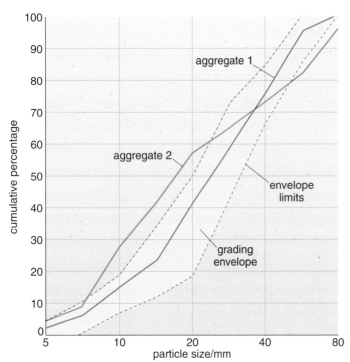

Figure 6.13   Particle size distribution curves for two aggregates, relative to permissible limits defined by the maximum and minimum limits of a grading envelope (note the particle size increases to the right). Aggregate 1 satisfies the specifications of the grading envelope, whereas aggregate 2 does not (in some fractions the line lies outside the envelope limits). The steeper the curve, the smaller the range of particle sizes; the narrower the grading envelope, the more precisely the aggregate size ranges are specified.

4   *Surface texture*: cement will stick to most rocks. Indeed, for many purposes, even smooth flint pebbles make perfectly satisfactory concrete aggregates, but a rough surface texture makes the best bond to cement. Fine particles such as clay minerals or dust from crushing have to be kept to a minimum (less than 5%), as they tend to coat the aggregate particles and prevent the cement from bonding well.

5   *Physical suitability*: exclusion of unsuitable fragments, such as high-porosity rock (susceptible to frost damage), or weak, easily crushed material, is essential.

6   *Chemical suitability*: aggregate must not react chemically with cement. Unfortunately, as cement sets it produces highly alkaline solutions that react with some siliceous rocks (e.g. flint and volcanic glass). This alkali–silica reaction forms a gel that can exert an internal pressure as high as $14\,\mathrm{MN\,m^{-2}}$ on the concrete, causing cracking. Salt (NaCl) makes the cement even more alkaline, so marine gravels must be thoroughly washed before being used for concrete. Common sulphide minerals (e.g. iron pyrites, FeS_2) can also react with cement to form corrosive sulphuric acid.

In the UK, most concrete is delivered from 'ready-mix' plants to a local area. Delivery is usually limited to a radius of about 20–30 km because once water has been added to cement the concrete must be poured within 2 hours. Local aggregate is preferred to minimize transport costs, so sites supplying aggregate must be widespread, and even more abundant near areas of high demand (e.g. cities). Concrete for special purposes, commanding a higher price, may use higher-quality aggregates from more remote sources.

Question 6.3

Which *two* of the following rock types would be least suitable as an aggregate for high-strength concrete, and why?

flint	equigranular, crystalline gneiss
slate	fine-grained granite
poorly cemented, porous sandstone	well-lithified quartzite

What type of aggregate is used in your local concrete — sands and gravels, or crushed rock? What are the main rock types it contains? A visit to your local builders' merchants or 'ready-mix' concrete plant should help you find out. Around Milton Keynes, local river valley sand and gravel deposits are widely used, dominated by larger pebbles of flint with some fragments of Jurassic limestone. Higher-quality concrete contains aggregates from further north, including crushed igneous rock from Charnwood, Leicestershire (Figure 6.14).

Figure 6.14   Aggregates for concrete: crushed igneous rock from Charnwood, Leicestershire (left); river gravels with rounded quartz pebbles (right).

6.6.3   Aggregates for roads

● What proportion of the aggregate used in the UK is used for road-building?

○ About one-third.

● How many tonnes would be needed for a new 20 km stretch of motorway?

○ Up to 2 million tonnes (Table 6.2).

These two figures highlight the extent to which road-building dominates the aggregate market. In a small, highly populated, industrialized country such as the UK, this demand is most keenly felt because of the high concentration of roads. The world average density of paved road is just less than 1 km per 10 km². In North America, it is about twice as high; in the EU as a whole, about 8 times as high; and in the UK, about 16 times as high. In SE England it is about four times as high as the UK average, which is over 30 times as high as the average for North America. So huge volumes of aggregate are needed for roads, and both the roads themselves and the aggregate quarries take up scarce land in the most densely populated area of the country.

Before discussing the supply of aggregates used in the construction and repair of roads, let's consider how stone is used in modern highways. Modern roads, which are still based on the principles laid down in the 18th century by John McAdam, are of two types:

- a *rigid* road, made from a series of short, cast slabs of *concrete* that are prepared from carefully graded stone fragments and sand bound with cement;

- a *flexible* bitumen-bound **macadam** ('tarmacadam') road, laid in long, smooth stretches, built up from a series of firmly consolidated layers of *aggregate bound with bitumen* (commonly termed asphalt).

Bitumen-bound and concrete road surfaces built on thick foundations can bear heavy traffic, but in both cases the cardinal principles established by McAdam have to be followed — the road must have:

- a firm, load-bearing base, composed of well-graded broken stone that compacts well and is not susceptible to frost damage or liable to absorb water like clay does;

- a dry foundation, with a raised roadbed to improve drainage;

- a hard-wearing, ideally waterproof, surface layer.

Although McAdam did not use binder for the road surface, the use of tar is crucial to modern road surfaces, where faster speeds demand a well-bound, high-friction surface for braking. Heavier axle loadings mean that modern roads have to be stronger (and hence thicker), so more aggregates are needed. As the road surface is made of bound gravel, it is likely to wear faster then a Victorian cobbled street made of solid blocks ('setts') of granite.

Before a modern road can be laid, the ground must be levelled off to an appropriate gradient: shallow gradients are preferred to ease traffic flow. If the ground surface is very soft, it must be covered with sand or broken rock as a capping layer, providing a foundation for the road proper. At this stage the

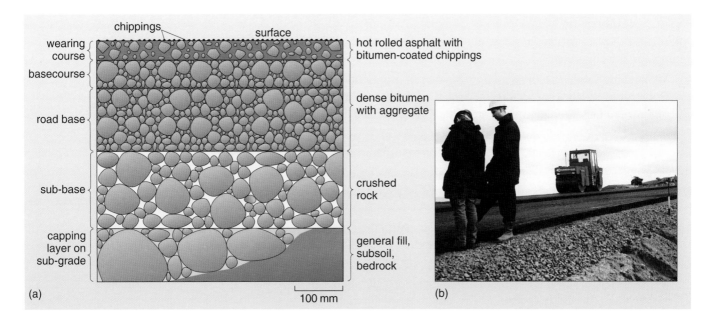

Figure 6.15 (a) Cross-section through the road pavement (above the capping layer) of a modern tarmacadam road. (b) Photograph showing the layered structure of the A1 in Northumberland: capping layer of reddish gravels (lower right); sub-base of unbound grey dolerite chippings (from the Whin Sill); road base of black bituminous tarmacadam; basecourse (under steamroller).

drainage is also set out, and if necessary the capping layer is built up above the water level in the ground. The capping layer is covered by a four-layer structure (sometimes known as the **road pavement**; Figure 6.15) comprising from bottom to top:

- **sub-base**: well drained with no binder, leaving spaces to prevent water being drawn up into the road; it provides the level surface for the upper layers of the road;

- **road base** and **basecourse**: coarse-grained, high crushing-strength aggregate (maximum diameter 40 mm) in a dense bituminous macadam, compacted to less than 7% porosity for good load-bearing characteristics. These may be combined into a single layer;

- **wearing course**: waterproof, fine-grained asphalt with skid-resistant rock chips, up to 20 mm in diameter, rolled into its surface to give high friction to the final road surface; it must not deform under braking conditions.

In rigid roads, a single concrete layer replaces the three upper layers.

The details of materials used in these layers are shown in Table 6.4.

Table 6.4 Relative proportions of materials used in a modern tarmacadam road.

	Thickness/mm	Maximum size aggregate/mm	Aggregate	Sand	Filler/granular $CaCO_3$	Bitumen
wearing course (asphalt)	15–50	20*	30%	52%	10%	8%
basecourse	50–80	40	95%	0	0	4.7%
road base	100–200	40	96%	0	0	3.5–4%
sub-base	250	75	100%	0	0	0
capping layer	300–500	125	local 'fill'	0	0	0

* The size of the skid-resistant chips depends on the thickness of the wearing course.

6.6.4 Physical testing of aggregates

Aggregates used in macadam roads need many of the same properties as aggregates for concrete:

1 *Shape*: equidimensional, angular crushed rock fragments that pack down to a strong interlocking texture. The rounded pebbles in most natural gravels are less suitable, but cheaper local gravels may be used for the lower layers, or roads carrying light loads.

2 *Size*: maximum aggregate particle size decreases from sub-base to wearing course.

3 *Grading*: aggregates should be well graded to form dense layers when compacted by heavy rolling equipment.

4 *Porosity*: rocks with a high porosity are unsuitable because they may suffer frost damage.

5 *Density*: generally, the denser the rock type, the more expensive it is to transport because transportation is charged by weight, but roadstone is ordered by volume. Hence basalt (density: $2.9\,\mathrm{t\,m^{-3}}$) can be 10% more expensive to transport than limestone (density: $2.6\,\mathrm{t\,m^{-3}}$).

6 *Surface texture*: most rocks have rough surfaces that bond well with tar; sandstones, quartzites and igneous rocks are among the best. Most crushed aggregates adhere better to tar than rounded pebbles (especially smooth flint) from natural gravels.

7 *Crushing strength*: all road aggregates must have high crushing strength, neither cracking nor crushing to a powder where fragments touch each other as loads pass over.

8 *Resistance to abrasion*: the wearing-course aggregate must have high resistance to abrasion, i.e. not be easily worn down (eroded) by rubber wheels.

9 *Resistance to polishing*: although some strong rocks resist abrasion well, they may become smooth and polished if used on a road surface, allowing vehicles to skid.

Aggregates must perform consistently under demanding conditions in flexible roads, so a series of special British Standard tests ensures that each aggregate has properties appropriate to its application. Tests are used to assess the last three properties in the list above.

Crushing strength is important but roads need to resist repeated dynamic loads rather than the static loading on, for instance, concrete pillars in a skyscraper. A widely used laboratory test involves 15 blows of a 14 kg steel 'hammer' dropped from a height of 380 mm onto small (10–14 mm) chips of the aggregate (Figure 6.16). The amount of fine material (< 2.4 mm) produced in the test, expressed as a percentage of the original sample, is the **aggregate impact value (AIV)**:

- the *lower* the AIV, the *higher* the strength of the aggregate;
- for any roadstone, an *AIV of less than 35%* is needed.

Resistance to abrasion is laboratory tested by mounting aggregate chips in resin to make a 'pad'. This pad is then held against a rotating disc, under the

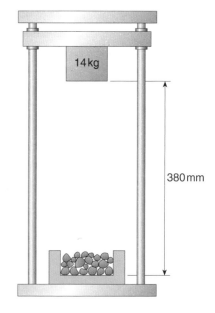

Figure 6.16 Aggregate impact value test apparatus. The 'hammer' is shown lifted ready to fall onto the rock chips in the tray below. After 15 such blows, a 2.4 mm sieve is used to separate any small fragments (fines) generated in the test, which are then weighed. A smaller mass of fragments indicate better performance and lower AIV.

abrasive action of wet sand (standard silica sand from Leighton Buzzard, UK) for 500 revolutions. The **aggregate abrasion value (AAV)** is the weight percentage of the original aggregate sample lost during the test:

- the *lower* the AAV, the *better* the wearing properties;
- for a good wearing-course aggregate an *AAV of less than 14%* is needed (sometimes as low as 10%).

Resistance to polishing is assessed by a similar test. Curved, mounted aggregate samples are held against a rotating rubber wheel, which is fed with fine wet abrasive for a set time (a few hours). The sample is then mounted on the base-plate of an apparatus (Figure 6.17) that tests its friction by measuring the drag it exerts on a pendulum that swings across the sample. This value for the friction, converted to a percentage, is the **polished stone value (PSV)**:

- the *higher* the PSV, the *better the resistance to polishing*;
- for a good wearing course, the *PSV should be greater than 60%*, often values as high as 70% are called for.

Skid resistance is increasingly tested by machines on actual road surfaces, as well as on aggregate samples.

The relationships between PSV, AAV and AIV are difficult to predict for an individual aggregate. However, Figure 6.18 shows two graphs that allow comparison of the typical ranges of these properties for different rock types. Figure 6.18a shows that most aggregates with higher PSV also tend to have low AIV, both of which are desirable for roadstone.

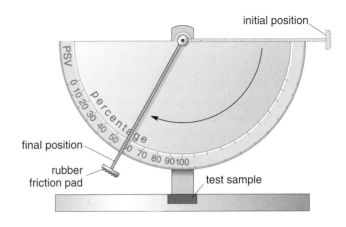

Figure 6.17 PSV test apparatus. The friction of the test pad retards the swing of the pendulum; in this case the PSV = 60. The smoother the test pad, the further the pendulum swings and the lower the PSV of the sample.

Figure 6.18 (a) Graph of PSV against AIV showing the typical range of values for different rock types. (b) A similar graph of typical PSV and AAV for different rock types. The limits for wearing course (solid line) and general roadstone (dashed line) aggregates are also marked in both (a) and (b). Hornfels is a hard, equigranular, fine-grained metamorphic rock.

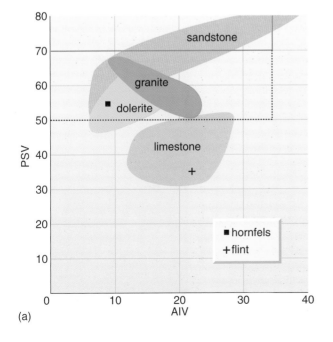

(a)

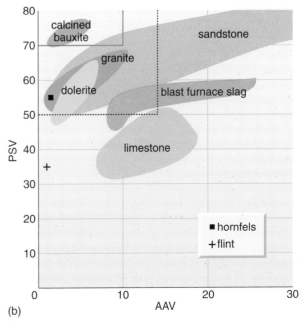

(b)

● For each rock type, how does AAV generally vary with PSV, and what implications does this relationship have for selecting wearing-course aggregates?

◐ In general, as PSV for each rock type increases, the AAV also increases significantly. This means that very few rocks with a PSV suitable for use in the wearing course (> 70%) have an AAV low enough to meet the standard for wearing-course aggregate (< 14%).

Many strong crystalline rocks have a PSV too low for many roadstone applications; on the other hand this is an advantage when they are polished as decorative slabs.

The maximum AAV and minimum PSV recommended for wearing-course aggregates for different situations are given in Table 6.5. These detailed criteria aim to account for the level of traffic usage and the demands of particular road sections, such as the locations where friction is crucial, particularly junctions and bends.

Table 6.6 compares typical test values for some aggregates used in Britain.

For potential wearing-course aggregates, PSV is crucial. Glassy flint and soft limestone polish too easily (Figure 6.19a), but both may be used in the lower layers of a road. In igneous rocks and quartzite, any softer mineral grains wear faster than hard ones, leaving an uneven upper surface on the aggregate particle that increases the micro-friction of the road surface (Figure 6.19b). The highest PSV rocks are all sandstones with angular quartz (sand) grains on their wearing surfaces, though Millstone Grit crumbles too easily to be a roadstone. Arkose and greywacke are both very well-cemented sandstones, with the optimum mixture of hard quartz grains in a slightly softer matrix (feldspar in the arkose; clay minerals, micas and small rock fragments in the greywacke). With tyre wear, grains drop out before they become polished, but not so fast that the aggregate wears away quickly (Figure 6.19c). Few natural rocks have PSV >70%, so calcined bauxite (roasted aluminium ore) is commonly used instead for specialized braking surfaces (naturally beige but often stained red) such as at junctions, roundabout approaches, and deceleration lanes.

There is also a macro-scale effect wherever aggregate chippings stick out of the road surface (Figure 6.19d), particularly if their edges are not easily rounded off. In concrete road surfaces, high-PSV materials are generally not used; instead, thin grooves cut across the road surface at right-angles to the traffic flow increase surface friction, making these roads very noisy to drive on.

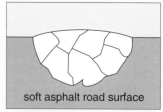

one mineral:
poor micro-friction

soft asphalt road surface

(a) limestone

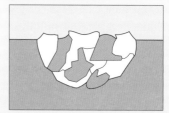

several different minerals:
good micro-friction

(b) coarse igneous rock

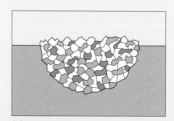

(c) greywacke

1 cm

(d)

Figure 6.19 Aggregate fragments in wearing-course asphalt after considerable use: (a) limestone — low PSV; heavily worn, smooth, polished surface (poor macro- and micro-friction); (b) coarse-grained igneous rock — high PSV; little wear — irregular top surface maintained by faster erosion of softer mineral grains, leaving harder grains sticking up (good macro- and micro-friction); (c) greywacke — highest PSV; rough surface of sharp quartz grains is always maintained by slow but constant loss of occasional grains being 'plucked' out by traffic, but the grains are well cemented so that wear is only slow (good macro- and excellent micro-friction); (d) macro-friction exhibited by rock chippings sticking up from soft asphalt next to a Shap granite sett whose surface is worn smooth. (a), (b) and (c) are all to the same scale.

Table 6.5 Maximum AAV and minimum PSV for wearing courses on various road sections.

Road type and situation	% of UK roads	Traffic density/ commercial vehicles per lane per day	Maximum AAV for wearing course/%	Minimum PSV for wearing course/%
deceleration lanes on high-speed roads (e.g. approaching traffic lights, and pedestrian crossings)	0.1	<250	14	63–65
		250–750	12	68
		>750	12	70
junctions, roundabouts and bends	4	<250	14	50–55
		250–750	12	55–60
		750–1750	12	63–65
		>1750	10	68–70
straight sections of motorways, dual carriageways and trunk roads	15	<750	12	55
		750–3250	10	57–65
		>3250	10	68
minor roads (not deceleration locations)	81	<250	14	50
		250–750	12	53
		750–1750	12	55–60
		>1750	10	63–68

Table 6.6 AIV, AAV and PSV values for some aggregates used in British roads.

Rock type	Location of quarry	AIV	AAV	PSV	Disadvantages
granite	Shap (Cumbria)	23	3.5	54	liable to shatter
granite	Glensanda (Scotland)	23	4	54	liable to shatter
'granite'*	Charnwood (Leicestershire)	10	10	66	
basalt	Antrim (N. Ireland)	15	6	57	slowly polished
dolerite	Belford (Northumberland)	8	3	57	slowly polished
quartzite	Wrekin (Shropshire)	21	5	57	liable to shatter
limestone	Derbyshire (Carboniferous)	23	14	38	soft: low wear resistance
flint	Berkshire	23	1	35	liable to shatter
sandstone	Yorkshire ('Millstone Grit'†)	29	26	72	poorly cemented, crumbles
arkose‡	Ingleton (Yorkshire)	11	5	62	
'greywacke'‡	Welsh borders	16	9	72	
calcined bauxite	imported (e.g. from China, Guyana)	33	4	75	

* Not a true granite, but a tough igneous rock that is often called 'granite' in the aggregate business.

† A coarse-grained sandstone, which has excellent skid resistance but poor strength.

‡ These are tough recrystallized sandy sediments of Silurian or Ordovician age that are both often called 'greywacke' or 'gritstone' in the aggregate business. They are widely used for skid-resistant road surfaces.

Question 6.4

(a) On what proportion of UK roads would the Derbyshire Carboniferous limestone be suitable as a wearing-course aggregate, and why?

(b) On which UK roads could Leicestershire 'granite' be used as a wearing-course aggregate?

6.6.5 UK distribution of wearing-course aggregates

⬤ Do the aggregates in the last three rows of Table 6.6 have a higher or lower place value than most other rocks in the table?

◯ They have a much *lower* place value; their special properties increase their value so they can be transported economically to more distant markets. Most of the other rocks in Table 6.6 are mainly used locally as cheap bulk aggregates.

Demand for higher-specification materials for modern road surfaces has led to some high-PSV aggregates being transported great distances, or traded internationally, at premium prices of almost £200 per tonne. In the UK, the chief demand for such materials is in densely populated SE England, which lacks rocks suitable for use in wearing courses (Figure 6.20). The younger rocks of the southeast are either too soft (limestones), polish much too easily (flint) or are poorly cemented sandstones that are unable to resist wear. Therefore high-PSV rocks suitable for wearing-course aggregate, such as igneous rocks, or sandstones older than 400 Ma that have been toughened by cementation and recrystallization during deep burial, have to be transported from outcrops in the north and west.

Some high PSV wearing-course aggregate is transported in bulk by sea to SE England. A Devonian-age (354–417 Ma) sandstone, quarried since the early 1990s at Leahill on the north side of Bantry Bay, southern Ireland, is not only exported to London, but has also been shipped to France, Germany, the Netherlands, Poland and Spain. Large, 75 000 tonne vessels can be loaded directly from the coastal quarry site for cheap transport to Europe. Granite from Glensanda in the Western Highlands of Scotland (Table 6.6), another remote coastal location, has been shipped as crushed rock aggregate in bulk to distant markets, including Texas, USA.

⬤ How can it be economic to open a new aggregate quarry in a remote coastal location where there is virtually no local market for aggregates?

◯ The output will go directly into ships, which are by far the cheapest method of bulk transport for long distances. Thus large quantities of cheap aggregate reach the market, undercutting the price of other potential wearing-course aggregates.

In fact, rock from Glensanda and Leahill can be delivered to European ports at a price that is competitive for other uses besides roads; for instance, Glensanda granite from London depots was used extensively in the concrete lining for the Channel Tunnel.

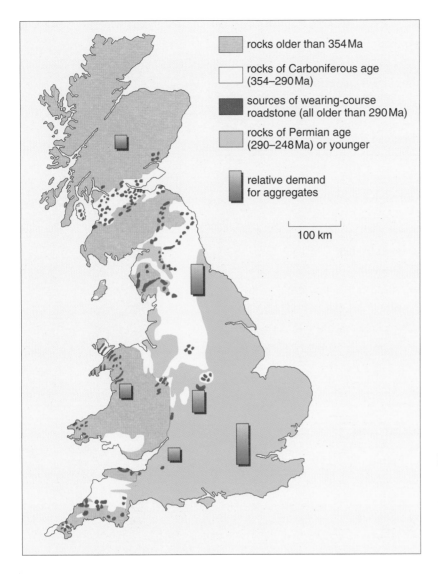

Figure 6.20 Distribution of rocks suitable for wearing-course aggregates in mainland Britain, and the ages of the rocks. The relative demand for these aggregates is shown by the height of the columns for four areas of England (southeast, southwest, midlands and north), Wales and Scotland.

At Leahill, markets have even been found for the waste fines (dust) generated during quarrying and processing. Some of the fines are shipped to the UK for use in some asphalts, in lightweight concrete blocks, and even artificial soils, reflecting a move towards more sustainable resource use (Chapter 7).

6.7 Summary of Chapter 6

1 Demand for aggregates rose rapidly during the 20th century. The current annual consumption in the UK of about 4 tonnes per capita is towards the lower end of the range for industrialized countries.

2 'Primary aggregates' (sands and gravels, and crushed rock) have been the traditional materials used for aggregates, but the usage of waste materials and recycled aggregates is increasing.

3 Properties of sands and gravels (e.g. grain size and degree of sorting) determine their behaviour in use and reflect the geological conditions under which the deposits were formed.

4 In some heavily populated areas, where sands and gravels have traditionally met the local aggregate demand, planning permission for future extraction is increasingly difficult to obtain.

5 Crushed rock aggregates are now consumed in larger quantities than sands and gravels, and are used largely in concrete and road construction where their high crushing strength is an advantage.

6 A rock for crushing to make aggregate should be of a low porosity to prevent frost damage, and be unable to react chemically with cement.

7 Aggregates for concrete-making must have fragments in a range of sizes (i.e. be well graded in the engineering sense), to pack down into a strong, low-porosity mass.

8 Aggregates for roads must have a high crushing strength, measured as its aggregate impact value (i.e. a low AIV) in a dynamic test.

9 Aggregates or chippings on a road surface must have high resistance to abrasion, measured as the aggregate abrasion value (i.e. a low AAV), and have high friction, measured as the polished stone value (i.e. a high PSV).

10 High-PSV aggregates are not available in many places in the UK, so some aggregate has to be brought long distances — especially to the southeast of England.

A SUSTAINABLE FUTURE FOR MINERALS? 7

7.1 The future of aggregate supplies

The rapid rise in UK aggregate consumption through the 20th century (Figure 6.2) has led to concerns about meeting future demands for aggregate. At the same time, the industry has changed its scale of operation from local to regional, national or even international, and capital investment has risen markedly. However, aggregate reserves are vast: the main issues for the future of aggregate supplies are more political, social and environmental than geological.

7.1.1 Sand and gravel

Sand and gravel deposits are quite widespread and cheap to extract. They are usually extracted from local pits close to their market due to their high place value. In large countries where land is not at a premium, this mode of extraction presents no problems. The vast gravel deposits at the margins of the Himalayas are easy pickings compared to river terrace gravels in the UK, where competition for land use is fierce. Lowland deposits near population centres in the UK are strictly regulated, and county councils maintain an up-to-date plan of land in their area that is available for aggregate working. Proven, economic reserves with permission for extraction (the land bank: see Section 6.4) were originally maintained for 10 years' supplies. However, by 2000 the national recommended level had been reduced to 7 years as the perceived need to plan long-term for inland aggregates diminished. Not all councils could meet this target: for example, in 2000 the Northamptonshire land bank was less than 2.5 years.

- What factors have made it possible to sustain reduced land banks at this time?

- Firstly, a general levelling-off of demand for all aggregates (Figure 6.2), and secondly an *increase* in other sources such as marine aggregates and crushed rock shipped from remote 'superquarries' (see Section 7.1.3) such as Glensanda or Leahill.

In fact, the development of these other sources of aggregate was partly in response to increasing pressure from local residents against sand and gravel extraction in their area, especially in lowland areas where heavy extraction had already taken place. Disputes caused by this NIMBY ('not in my backyard') attitude may be resolved at a local level, but in densely populated SE England this is increasingly difficult. The legacy of flood-plain extraction is flooded pits, which may be restored to other uses such as nature reserves and/or recreational amenities. However, precious land is still lost, so there is a tendency to restrict flood-plain extraction (as in the Nene Valley, Box 7.1), and to work deposits where the land can be fully restored.

Seabed dredging superficially seems to be the perfect, 'out of sight, out of mind' solution to the NIMBY problem. However, environmental concerns have generated considerable opposition to the practice, notably from the UK fishing industry that is already facing declining fish stocks. Research has shown

Box 7.1   Aggregate planning in Northamptonshire

In Northamptonshire, around three times more sand and gravel was extracted between 1991 and 2001 than crushed rock (mainly Jurassic limestone and some ironstone). The Nene Valley is the traditional site of extraction, with extensive flooded old pits that prompted a policy in 1991 to discourage further new workings, despite high demand for aggregate from major towns in the region. Other reserves were sought to meet the anticipated demand, including glacial deposits above the valley floor that could be restored to agriculture by returning the topsoil and landscaping (Figure 7.1).

However, demand for aggregates fell from the mid-1990s, so that in the period 1991–2001,

Northamptonshire's average annual production of sand and gravel was only 1.5 million tonnes, rather than the planned 2.25 million tonnes. Crushed rock production also fell, though at a slower rate, which was consistent with national trends (Figure 6.3). Part of the decrease in production of these natural aggregates reflected increasing usage of recycled or alternative materials for aggregate in the county.

In early 2004, a draft minerals plan placed more emphasis on processing recycled and waste materials to supplement natural aggregates to raise their contribution from around 10% to the government's target of 23% by 2016. Lower targets for aggregate production meant that less material would be needed to maintain 7-year land banks. The plan also named several unexploited valley areas to be protected from future extraction, including short stretches of the Nene Valley, and aimed to exploit glacial deposits rather than river valleys for sand and gravel.

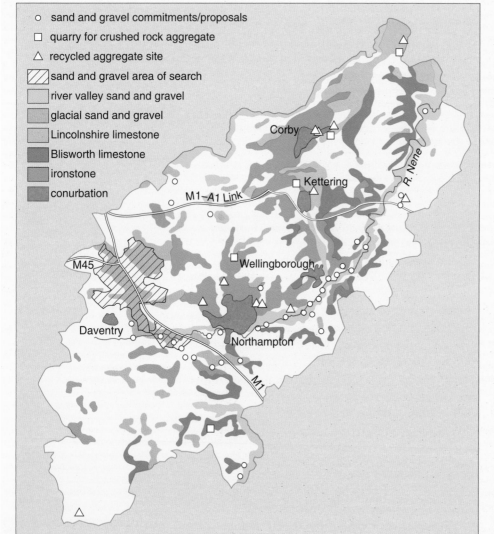

Figure 7.1   Location map showing major towns, sand and gravel workings, quarries producing crushed rock aggregate, and sites licensed to produce aggregate from recycled waste in Northamptonshire. Also shown is an area where glacial gravels are to be exploited ('area of search').

dredging to be detrimental to local marine life, not only in the removal of seabed material, but also in discharging unwanted sediment (e.g. fines) into coastal waters. Coastal erosion may increase if huge tonnages of sea-floor sediment are removed from areas just offshore, as was dramatically illustrated in south Devon in the early 20th century. Following offshore dredging for shingle, the beach at Hallsands fell by 3.5 m and the village was exposed to the full force of the waves; 29 houses were reduced to rubble. To minimize the threat of erosion, most licensed dredging areas in the UK are at least 6 miles offshore, in water over 20 m deep. Some dredged aggregate is used directly for 'beach nourishment' to combat coastal erosion — over 20 million tonnes of marine aggregate was used on Britain's beaches throughout the 1990s. Partnerships between the aggregate producers and wildlife organizations help reduce environmental impacts by funding research into the effects of dredging. Increasing proportions of the aggregate are exported to Holland and Belgium, although gravel extraction in UK waters has been roughly constant during the 1990s. Marine aggregates are a finite resource: UK reserves are estimated at around 50 years at current extraction rates — and only Japan was producing more marine aggregates in the early 2000s.

7.1.2   Crushed rock aggregates

Although UK demand for aggregate levelled off in the 1990s, the demand for aggregate from quarries still far outstrips our other quarrying needs. Economic pressures in the industry (including the Aggregates Levy, see Box 7.2) favour large, modern operations over small, local quarries. Where land is at a premium, as in densely populated areas of the UK, this presents a problem. Moreover, many traditional quarrying areas lie in scenic areas that are low in employment opportunities. Carboniferous limestone for example has been worked for many years in regions such as the Yorkshire Dales and the Mendips south of Bristol. As demand for crushed rock has increased, many quarries have become very large, working layers of limestone up to 100 m thick, and making large scars in the local scenery.

Box 7.2   Taxing extraction: the Aggregates Levy

In a bid to encourage a shift from primary aggregate to recycled and secondary aggregates, in 2002 the UK Government introduced a tax of £1.60 per tonne of primary aggregate produced. At that time, rates of aggregate tax in six other EU countries ranged from 42p per tonne (Denmark) to 6p per tonne (France). Marine sand and gravel was taxed, as well as inland sand, gravel, and crushed rock. Many other materials (e.g. slate, china clay, silica sand, building stone, limestone for cement-making) were exempt from the tax.

The revenue generated was used to reduce the employers' National Insurance contributions and to set up a Sustainability Fund to ameliorate the negative environmental effects of aggregate extraction. The aim was to finance mainly local community projects near current or disused extraction sites, focusing on four principal themes:

- landscape and community recreation;
- habitat restoration and local biodiversity;
- restoration and protection of historic environment;
- pollution mitigation.

Projects funded from an annual fund of around £28 million range from providing a playground in a Leicestershire village adjacent to a quarry, to improving access and deterring predators on a shingle beach nature reserve in East Sussex. The fund has also financed excavations of ice-age remains — including woolly rhinos and mammoths from sand and gravel pits in Norfolk and the Midlands.

Nowadays, even permissions to extend existing UK quarries require **environmental impact assessments**, typically incorporating surveys of habitats, invertebrates, breeding birds, mammals, and plant species. Local perceptions of quarrying differ from a desecration of scenic landscapes to welcome jobs and a boost to the local economy. These conflicts comprise the first environmental issue: *the location of the rock to be quarried.*

The land needed each year for even a medium-sized quarry is extensive, and results in a large hole if quarrying continues for many years (Figure 7.2). In an area with many quarries, the impact on scenery can become excessive, so restoration must be considered before planning permission is granted for a new quarry. Since sedimentary strata tend to be limited in thickness, the visual impact cannot be minimized just by quarrying deeper, nor may it be possible simply to open a quarry elsewhere if a suitable rock is not available. To maintain consumption of crushed rock aggregate at levels of the early 2000s (Figure 6.3), the UK needs the equivalent of about 230 medium-sized quarries.

Figure 7.2 (a) Image of a large quarry for crushed rock aggregate, showing its extent in 1998 and a proposed extension.

(b) Image illustrating how the quarry may look following planned restoration.

Transport — especially road haulage — can be a contentious issue at large quarries.

Question 7.1

Imagine that a quarry sent all its annual output of 600 000 t in 20 t lorry loads through an adjacent village. How frequently would vehicles pass through the village, assuming 250 working days a year and an 8-hour working day?

This highlights the second environmental issue: the *method of transporting* the aggregate to market. Some larger inland quarries, which produce between one million and five million tonnes a year, deliver much of their output by rail in special trains that can take up to 3000 t in a single shipment. This not only dramatically reduces road traffic near the quarry, but also enables the aggregate to be supplied to markets much further afield because bulk distribution rail freight is cheaper than road (see Table 2.1). Figure 7.3 shows the pattern of transport by rail that brought aggregates from SW England and Leicestershire to London and the southeast in the late 1980s.

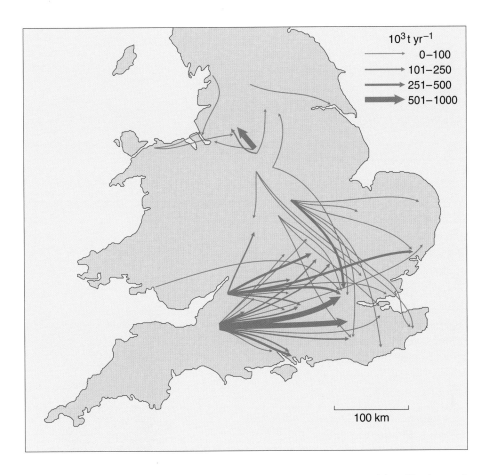

Figure 7.3 Major rail movements of crushed rock aggregates from inland quarries in England and Wales in the late 1980s. Figures quoted are in thousands of tonnes per year.

Use the geological map of the UK (Figure 2.6) to try to identify the main rock units being exploited as aggregates for use in the southeast in Figure 7.3.

This is tricky, as the crucial outcrops are very small on the map. Most of the rock from the southwest comes from two areas of Carboniferous limestone, one in the Mendips south of Bristol, and the other north of Bristol. The other source for aggregate is a very small outcrop of hard granite and volcanic rocks surrounded by soft Triassic rocks around Charnwood, Leicestershire.

The third major environmental issue is the *sustainability* of the quarrying operation in the future, which is affected by several factors: future demand for quarry output, changing industry conditions and costs, and political and environmental constraints. These factors can act on several scales. For instance, political changes may be:

- local (e.g. planning authorities, Box 7.1);
- national (e.g. legislation to encourage the use of recycled materials);
- international (e.g. EU directives on quarrying).

Two solutions to the environmental pressures of large quarries employ radically different approaches: the development of either remote, coastal superquarries or underground stone mines.

7.1.3 Coastal superquarries

In many cases, rock suitable for use as aggregate is found far from the major population centres, i.e. the main markets. Transporting the aggregate from quarry to market becomes a serious issue, both in terms of traffic volume and cost. For extraction at a remote site to be economic, the quarry output must be large; even with modern, mechanized methods, this implies a huge site.

● How might the transport costs be reduced for such an isolated quarry?

◐ By using cheap modes of transport, such as bulk shipping by rail or sea.

The solution in the UK was to aim to site large quarries on the coast, where rock could be extracted and loaded directly onto bulk ocean-going carriers for cheap transportation to national or international markets. As Figure 7.4 shows, there are a number of geologically suitable sites for such coastal superquarries in Scotland, although by 2004 still only one quarry (Glensanda) was in production. Glensanda has even shipped crushed granite to Houston, Texas, but this transatlantic export has ceased, partly due to the development of similar coastal superquarries in the USA and Mexico. Ships of up to 60 000 tonnes capacity supply the coastal cities of southeastern USA with granite from Nova Scotia and limestone from the Bahamas. Meanwhile, Glensanda has been continuously operational since 1986. So why have no other superquarries appeared in the UK?

One major reason is *economic*: demand for aggregate has stagnated since the early 1990s, slowing the impetus for developing new superquarries. One casualty was a proposed superquarry at Jossingfjord, Norway, intended to supply Western Europe with crushed anorthosite, a tough igneous rock rich in feldspar. Although planning permission was granted, this site was still undeveloped in 2004 due to

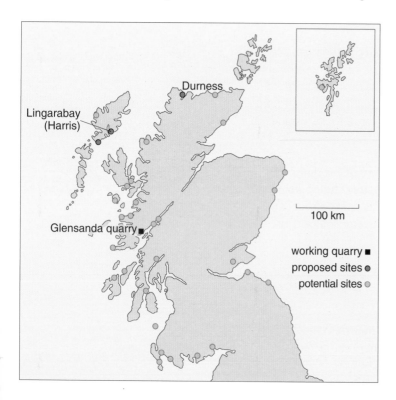

Figure 7.4 Some potential coastal superquarry sites in Scotland, a preliminary survey based largely on the geological suitability of the rock.

low demand. However, as pressure on the expansion of inland quarries increases, coastal superquarries may find favour once more.

The second curb on superquarry development is *environmental opposition*, notably to a site at Lingarabay on the island of Harris. Permission was initially sought in 1993 to exploit an anorthosite intrusion that was suitable for aggregate. It was ideally situated near a sheltered, natural deep-water harbour. Despite initial support from the local council, and following a public inquiry in 1994–5, planning permission was finally refused in the year 2000, and the company withdrew its plans entirely in early 2004. Much of this opposition can be put down to the proximity of the Lingarabay quarry to the main settlements on Harris, as opposed to Glensanda's relative isolation, demonstrating the power of the NIMBY attitude even with a 'backyard' whose community is very small. There was concern over pollution of the clean coastal waters of the Hebrides, and risks associated with increased shipping traffic in restricted sea lanes. Initial support for the project sprang from the desire for jobs and benefits to the local economy, but opponents of the scheme pointed out that many employees would be brought in from elsewhere, threatening traditional ways of life, as well as the tourist and fishing industries. For example, the quarrying company wanted to work through Sunday, which is against the strict Presbyterian beliefs of many islanders.

A further point is that the Lingarabay quarry was planned for opencast extraction and processing, with accompanying noise, dust and visual impact (Figure 7.5). By contrast, Glensanda is a more contained operation, with crushed rock transported from an open pit down a vertical shaft and by underground conveyor to the dockside; further quarrying will extend downwards rather than outwards. Is quarrying, perhaps, set to go underground?

Figure 7.5   (a) Roineabhal, a mountain above Lingarabay on the island of Harris, Outer Hebrides, which was proposed as the site of a coastal superquarry in the early 1990s. (b) Computer-generated image of the quarry in operation, produced by campaigners against the development.

7.1.4   Underground mines

The form of most igneous intrusions (as at Glensanda) encourages expansion of excavations downwards rather than outwards, which is in contrast to mines in relatively thin, but laterally extensive sedimentary beds. Subsurface mines in sedimentary rocks are thus often extensions of existing quarries, with tunnels driven into the old face (as at Bath, Section 2.4.2). A grid of galleries that are separated and supported by pillars allows 40–70% of the rock to be removed, with the size of the galleries determined largely by the rock strength. The

USA has pioneered large subterranean mines for crushed stone (there are 21 subsurface limestone mines in Kentucky alone, though not all produce crushed rock). Demand for aggregate in the USA increased steadily through the 1990s, in contrast to stagnant demand in the UK. Increased constraints on surface quarrying — in particular long and costly planning application procedures for quarry extensions — are driving many operations underground. Some mines have galleries large enough for conventional loaders and dump-trucks; this eases extraction, but also has implications for usage of the mines afterwards. Abandoned mines in the USA (chiefly in limestone) are used for archive storage, warehousing, and a variety of commercial applications (Figure 2.17).

The increasing pressure on inland quarries in the UK, and the negative publicity associated with the Lingarabay project, may encourage the development of large-scale subsurface mining for crushed rock aggregate in the future, despite the technical challenges and costs of extraction underground. Provided mining methods create a stable, regular underground space, the mine could have a new lease of life after extraction has ceased — exploiting all the advantages that have made Subtropolis successful in Kansas (Section 2.4.2).

7.2   Recycling waste materials

The issue of aggregate supply and consumption is just one of many concerns over the future of resource usage that has prompted governments to examine ways of making consumption more sustainable. In the case of aggregates, the UK Government has deployed two complementary pieces of legislation, the Aggregates Levy (2002) and the Landfill Tax (1996), to reduce extraction of primary materials and encourage the use of secondary aggregates from recycled waste materials. The Aggregates Levy (Box 7.2) adds to the cost of extracting fresh aggregate, while the Landfill Tax imposes a charge on disposal of waste to landfill (Box 3.3). Both use fixed rates per tonne of material. The aim is to change an industry which has traditionally been geared towards extracting primary aggregate, but is part of a broader initiative to encourage recycling at all levels. This section explores some of the issues in the developing field of recycling industrial and construction waste.

7.2.1   Recycled building materials

In past centuries, recycling of good quality building stone was second nature — the destruction of a castle, for example, produced a plentiful supply of dressed stone for the neighbouring town or village. Roman bricks — distinctively thinner than modern bricks — were recycled well into the Middle Ages. In the 20th century, population growth, the mass production of cheap construction materials, and higher engineering specifications have all contributed to a decline in recycling and an increase in the construction waste generated. Most demolition rubble (e.g. broken concrete and brick) is downgraded to general fill, perhaps for the footings of the new building, due to engineering specifications. Some valuable materials (e.g. roofing slate) may be sold on to reclamation yards for use in conservation areas or listed buildings, and original building stone may also be recycled.

7.2.2   Aggregates from waste

The introduction of the Aggregates Levy in the UK may encourage the conversion of more demolition wastes to aggregate that can be used in more specialized applications than simply basic fill.

Question 7.2

Imagine a scheme designed to recycle general demolition waste into aggregate for use in concrete.

(a) What processing would be needed to convert this waste into suitable aggregate?

(b) What additional costs would be incurred in recycling waste from a demolition site to another construction site or concrete casting factory?

(c) Which kind of operator would be most likely to implement such a recycling scheme: a large contractor involved in major construction projects, or a local builder?

Most projects in the UK that have pioneered recycling of materials for construction are on a large scale and are able to absorb the extra costs, but they are also more capable of attracting grants from governments or bodies like the EU that subsidize recycling initiatives. The benefits of on-site processing are illustrated by the recycling of concrete for sub-base aggregate via stockpiles at three London airports. From 1995 to 2002, the British Airports Authority recycled roughly 210 000 tonnes of concrete, at a total estimated saving of £1.8 m, which resulted in a reduction of 42 000 lorry journeys amounting to 1.85 million road miles. Another example is the M6 toll motorway around Birmingham, where the use of recycled and secondary aggregates reduced costs by over £16 million.

Another case where material can be recycled on-site is the use of **asphalt planings** generated during roadworks in the bitumen-bound layers of the new road. The following question is based on a small-scale project involving Norfolk County Council and the company Lafarge in England.

Question 7.3

(a) What direct saving would result from the substitution of recycled asphalt (at £6 per tonne) for primary aggregate (£11 per tonne) for a quantity of 5364 tonnes?

(b) What other costs will be saved by the use of recycled asphalt planings that would otherwise be sent to landfill?

(c) What other indirect benefits to road users, constructors or the local council might result from recycling asphalt planings in this way?

Not all industrial wastes are produced at the very site where they can be re-used as readily as asphalt planings; most of the 5 billion tonnes of industrial waste accumulated in the UK over the last few centuries is in spoil tips close to the original site of extraction. Table 7.1 lists the estimated size and locations of stockpiles of the principal industrial waste materials, and the rates at which they are being produced and used in the early 21st century.

Table 7.1   Some UK industrial waste materials and their uses in the early 21st century.

Waste	Location	Stockpile/ 10^6 t	Annual production/10^6 t	Annual use/ 10^6 t	Main uses
waste slate	North Wales, Cornwall, Lake District	950	7	<1	fill, road foundations
quarry waste	outside the southeast	?	36	2	fill
colliery spoil*	coalfields	3600	10	4	fill
pulverized fuel ash (PFA) and furnace bottom ash (FBA)†	coal-fired power stations	200	7	5	blocks, fill, cement substitute
incinerator bottom ash (IBA)‡	incinerator sites	0	3	<1	fill, blocks
iron and steel slags	industrial areas	30	4	6	aggregate
foundry sands	industrial areas	<1	1	<1	blocks, landfill covering
china clay sand	Cornwall, Devon	600	26	1.3	blocks, fill, aggregate
demolition rubble	widespread	0	70	40	fill, aggregate
asphalt road planings	widespread	<1	7	6	fill, aggregate
totals		>5380	171	~66	

* Much colliery waste has been left as conical hills, now landscaped and grassed over, and is unlikely ever to be used. Burnt 'red' shale is best; unburnt 'black' shale can ignite spontaneously due to its sulphide and carbon content, and is too soft for many purposes. Production has declined markedly as more coal is imported.

† PFA, which collects in power station chimneys, is pozzolanic; that is, it sets hard with water and so can be used as a cement substitute, in blocks or as a grout for filling cavities, such as old mines. FBA is used as a lightweight aggregate because it contains numerous small 'glass' spheres (cenospheres), which give it good thermal insulation properties.

‡ IBA from municipal waste incinerators.

Are these waste materials being generated faster than they are being used?

Most of the wastes are still being produced at a greater rate than they are being used, the main exception being iron and steel slags, where some stockpiled material is used in road-building.

Historically, the construction industry has tended to quarry fresh aggregate rather than use waste because it was almost always cheaper.

Why wasn't it cheaper to use a waste material that comes 'free' rather than dig out new materials?

One reason is that many wastes are too remote from potential construction sites for transportation to be economic: they have a high place value. They often also require costly processing to meet specifications for their re-use.

The influence of transport costs is being eroded by increasing environmental pressure — backed up by legislation — so that more and more of these stockpiles will be used, particularly if a cheap mode of bulk transport (railway, shipping) is available. For those industrial sites (and their waste tips) at a railhead, little capital investment is needed to provide the infrastructure. North Wales has an estimated 730 Mt of slate waste in the large heaps so typical of Blaenau Ffestiniog and the surrounding area. A major construction company, Alfred McAlpine, is planning (early 2000s) to use this waste as secondary aggregate, transporting it by rail on existing tracks. The scheme requires an investment of £16 million, but low rail costs and exemption of waste slate from the Aggregates Levy would make the scheme viable for an operation recycling up to 10 Mt annually. One contentious issue is that the waste material from crushed rock and limestone quarries is *not* exempt from the levy, so no cost benefits accrue in using it as secondary aggregate, though it is probably more suitable than slate for many applications.

This example highlights two other issues with using waste stockpiles. The first is *environmental*: some stockpiles have become an integral part of the landscape and may be an attraction for tourists or form specialized habitats worthy of conservation as nature reserves. The striking white piles of china clay waste around St Austell divided local opinion between affection and aversion (see Box 7.3). The second issue is *technical*: some wastes are not suitable for many end uses. In some cases, advances in technology can reduce this problem by improving old or inventing new processing methods to convert the waste into usable material. Furnace bottom ash (FBA) has been the focus of much research, partly due to an instinctive mistrust of its origin and, as a result, a wide range of uses have been developed (Figure 7.6). FBA has also been used in the insulating tiles on the USA shuttle spacecraft. Consequently, more is known about the properties and (minimal) hazards of furnace ashes than about most natural aggregates. In 2001, almost all FBA was recycled in some way, but only about half of the PFA.

At the turn of the 21st century, very little UK incinerator bottom ash (IBA) from municipal plants was recycled; by contrast, the Netherlands used almost 100% of its IBA as fill and in road construction.

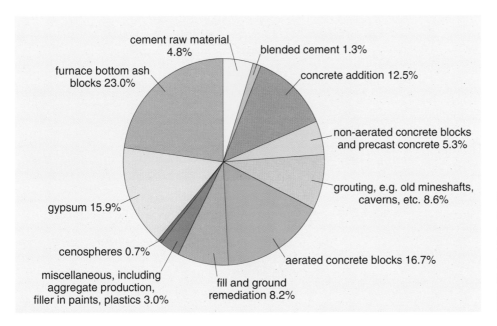

Figure 7.6   Proportion of UK furnace ash products sold for use in various applications, 2001. The gypsum is a by-product of 'scrubbing' the flue gases; 'cenospheres' are tiny glass spheres found in furnace bottom ash.

⬤ What advantage might IBA have over other potential secondary aggregates?

◐ Municipal incinerators are commonly sited close to large population centres, so waste stockpiles are close to potential markets, whereas most other industrial wastes (e.g. blast furnace bottom ash) are more remote.

Some waste materials are much more widely used in other countries; for instance many European countries use iron and steel slags extensively in road-building. This is largely due to lower standards of specification for secondary aggregates.

Box 7.3   Wastes from china clay production

China clay is an unusual clay deposit because the kaolinite itself forms only about 12% of the material extracted, the rest being waste: chiefly quartz (50%), mica (12.5%), decomposed granite fragments (12.5%) and overburden (13%); all of which have to be disposed of. The tradition has been to tip this waste, forming huge white hills known locally as the 'Cornish Alps' (Figure 7.7a). Local opinion was divided on these striking landscape features: some viewed them as adding character and interest to the local area, reflecting its industrial heritage, while to others they were an unwelcome sign of mining devastation. Most of the tips have now been landscaped with gentler contours, and planted to stabilize the slopes (Figure 7.7b). As a result, only 230 million tonnes of waste are available for use, from an estimated stockpile of over 600 million tonnes.

⬤ About 26 million tonnes (Table 7.1) of waste from the UK china clay industry is produced each year; why isn't it all used?

◐ Although this represents ~ 25% of the annual output from sand and gravel pits in the UK, the supply is too remote from most markets to be used economically.

These wastes have been used locally for many years to make cement blocks for house-building, but local demand for blocks is limited. Some china clay waste has also been used in the sub-base and as fill in road-building schemes within Cornwall. Inland transport costs limit the movement of wastes to markets within about 60 km, and so consumption of these wastes is only running at ~ 5% of their production (Table 7.1). However,

33 000 tonnes of china clay sand was shipped to London and the southeast in 2001. Many present-day workings simply use the waste materials to backfill pits that have been worked out.

(a)

(b)

Figure 7.7   (a) Waste tips at china clay workings in Cornwall: the 'Cornish Alps'. A flooded china clay pit can be seen to the upper left of the photograph.
(b) Landscaped china clay tips, 2004. In earlier times, the local rivers 'ran white' due to clay escaping from the clay separation processes.

Some relaxation of the UK's stringent specifications had already occurred by the year 2000, and further relaxation — along with advances in processing techniques — would allow much wider use of such materials, particularly in low-grade applications.

7.2.3   Other uses of wastes

Research into the use of PFA as a soil additive has shown many benefits, mainly in terms of improving the physical properties of the soil, such as water retention and workability. For some soils, PFA can be used to reduce acidity. Compared to natural soils, PFA is deficient only in carbon and nitrogen. Developing industrial countries such as India, which generate considerable amounts of furnace ash, could use large quantities of this waste product to boost their agriculture. FBA has a wide range of applications, including as a filler in paints and plastics, and in heat- or radiation-absorbing coatings.

Towards the end of the 20th century, environmental stewardship has passed to the international community, with a series of treaties designed to curb pollution and promote awareness of global environmental problems. With fossil fuel consumption a major target for these treaties, there is pressure on the building materials industry to reduce its fuel usage and develop alternative fuels that emit less greenhouse gases (predominately CO_2).

●   Which processes in the manufacture of building materials are particularly damaging in terms of fuel consumption and CO_2 emissions?

○   Any process that consumes fuel on a large scale, such as firing bricks, is harmful to the environment. However, cement production not only requires fuel for the high-temperature kilns, but *also* produces additional CO_2 by decarbonation of limestone during formation of cement clinker. It has been estimated that 8% of global CO_2 emissions are due to cement manufacture.

Both brick firing and cement kilns can use various wastes (e.g. scrap tyres, processed sewage waste, package waste) as fuel, thereby apparently easing two problems simultaneously, but such wastes still emit considerable amounts of CO_2. Again, advances in technology are required — for example at the start of the 21st century the production of fuel briquettes from sterilized putrescible waste is being developed. This process uses relatively low temperatures (~ 160°C) and steam to convert waste to a sterile, fibrous material that can be used as compost or converted to fuel briquettes. The advantage of this process over direct incineration is the low CO_2 emissions. A more indirect route has been followed near Barnsley in Yorkshire, where older clay pits have been filled with local domestic waste, and the landfill gas is collected for use in firing the brick kilns.

Solid wastes are not the only wastes that can be useful. Since the 1980s, many industrialized nations have passed waste gaseous sulphur emissions from power stations through limestone 'scrubbers' (Section 5.4) to produce pure calcium sulphate (gypsum). Desulphurization of flue gases contributes to a significant proportion of the UK's gypsum production (in the early 2000s), and is one important global source of secondary or 'recovered' sulphur. Sulphur is also obtained from petroleum refining. Production from primary sulphur deposits has fallen rapidly in the face of competition from these sources of recovered sulphur (Box 7.5).

Box 7.4 Bricks: a discreet dumping ground

Besides being used as fuel for firing, waste materials can also be added to bricks. There are three main categories of additive:

- *primary raw material*: any inert material (known as 'grog') that is added to supplement the raw clay;
- *internal fuel*: combustible material that is added to the brick clay to reduce primary fuel consumption (as with natural organic matter in the Oxford Clay; Section 3.3.3), and that may enhance some technical attributes, e.g. pore structure, colour;
- *body modifiers*: material that is added specifically to change the character of the fired brick by improving its technical or aesthetic qualities.

The natural variability of the clays used to make bricks means that brick-making can tolerate the addition of significant amounts of many types of wastes. For instance, crushed fired brick waste from brick-making itself has traditionally been added as grog to brick clay, with the benefit of quicker drying and firing cycles. Similar inert, fine-grained by-products of stone or aggregate processing could also be used as grog.

One innovative addition to bricks is processed sewage sludge, which can act as in-built fuel, reducing firing costs. Algoa Brick in South Africa was producing bricks with 30% sewage sludge in 2000, though the practice was also recorded in late 19th century Manchester, where colliery washings were used in a similar way to lower fuel costs.

PFA is added to bricks as a modifier to help reduce fluorine emissions from firing that can harm the local environment (Section 3.2.2). It can also accelerate drying and firing in the same way as crushed fired brick (grog). The ash content may be as high as 85–90%.

Other materials that can be added to bricks include dust from steel furnaces, tannery sludge and coconut pith. Any use of waste material must be financially beneficial to the producer, which generally means that the waste product must be cheaper than the primary raw material it is replacing once indirect factors such as landfill tax are taken into account.

Box 7.5 Sulphur: from product to by-product

Sulphur has been used for millennia as a pigment and in medicine, but it was best known in ancient times as the combustible element (its name means 'burning stone' in Latin), widely used in matches, fumigants, incendiaries, weapons and gunpowder. By contrast, its primary use in the modern world is for manufacturing fertilizers. Sulphur and sulphuric acid are so necessary to manufacturing that their demand can be used as an accurate index of a nation's business activity.

Sources

Native sulphur is precipitated from sulphurous gases emitted from volcanic fumaroles, but is only mined from this source in a few regions — Indonesia, the Philippines and the Andes — today (Figure 7.8).

Native sulphur formed by bacterial reduction of gypsum found capping salt domes was formerly extracted by the Frasch process. This process was developed in the late 1800s in southern USA. Superheated steam (170 °C) and air were pumped

Figure 7.8 Sulphur miner, Mount Ijen, East Java. Mining involves two to three 4-hour round-trips per day to the fumaroles, working in a noxious atmosphere beside an acidic crater lake (pH<1). Each miner's daily wage is around 2 US dollars.

down a series of nested tubes that were drilled into the deposit and forced liquid sulphur (melting point 113 °C) up to the surface. The last remaining Frasch sulphur mine in the USA closed in 2000 under the pressure of cheap recovered sulphur supplies, after dominating 20th century production. Another casualty of the competition from recovered sulphur is the roasting of the common mineral iron pyrites (FeS_2) to produce sulphuric acid (H_2SO_4). Environmental problems associated with these plants have led to their demise in most countries, except those with less-stringent pollution laws such as China. By 2002, only around 8% of the world's sulphuric acid was being manufactured from pyrites.

Many pyrites roasting plants were easily converted to use recovered elemental sulphur as a raw material for sulphuric acid production.

● Where does secondary (recovered) sulphur come from?

◐ Power station flue gas desulphurization has already been mentioned, and some sulphide smelting yields sulphuric acid from similar gaseous emissions. However, the main source is from the refining of crude oil and natural gas.

Average crude oil contains 1–3% dissolved sulphur, which is converted to hydrogen sulphide (H_2S) during refining, and thence to elemental sulphur or sulphuric acid. H_2S can form a high proportion (up to 60%) of natural gas (which is then called 'sour'). These sources of recovered sulphur have increased from negligible levels before 1960 to being the dominant sulphur source (approximately 80%) in the early 21st century (Figure 7.9). Oil and gas companies have therefore become the world's largest sulphur producers.

Production and uses

Approximately 60 Mt of sulphur are produced annually in all forms, of which around 70% is elemental. Increased global production in the latter half of the 20th century (similar to that shown in Figure 7.9) was due to escalating demand for fertilizers and included large quantities of recovered sulphur from Canadian gas fields. Although initially costly, recovering sulphur is now cheaper than primary extraction and recovered sulphur has exceeded demand.

● What effect will this excess production have on the price of sulphur?

◐ The price will tend to decrease. In fact, the price of sulphur has been steadily decreasing from around US$100 in the early 1980s, to a level of around US$35–40 per tonne in 2003.

Apart from making combustible products such as matches, sulphur is used to vulcanize rubber — making it stronger, more elastic, and increasing its friction on dry surfaces (crucial for tyres). Its antibiotic properties find uses in medicine (e.g. 'sulpha' drugs) and as fungicides. However, most sulphur is converted to sulphuric acid, which is widely used in the chemicals industry where it has a vast range of uses. Around 60–70% of sulphuric acid is used to manufacture 'superphosphate' fertilizers from naturally occurring phosphate deposits, and it is this major use that means demand for sulphur is likely to match world population growth. Fortunately, sulphur has many different potential sources, including gypsum and sulphates in seawater that are currently uneconomic, so it is expected that current trends in production and price can be maintained.

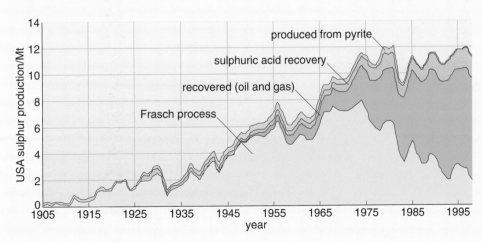

Figure 7.9   Sulphur production in the USA by source, 1905 to 1998. Note that Frasch production ceased in the year 2000.

The reduction in exploitation of primary sulphur resources shows that human ingenuity can drive technological advances that actively contribute to sustainable development. The degree to which this is possible varies from resource to resource, but many countries have recognized that the scale of consumption of materials, such as aggregates during the 20th century, cannot be sustained indefinitely. Already, in the early years of the 21st century, governments are legislating to drive a shift away from primary exploitation of resources towards the 'three Rs': *reduce*, *re-use* and *re-cycle*. While the damaging effects of fossil fuel consumption may grab the headlines, sustainability issues exist with all industrial minerals, and pressures will mount as long as the world's population grows. Humans have worked for millennia to shape their environment: in the future they must use the same ingenuity to preserve it.

7.3   Summary of Chapter 7

1   Although demand for aggregate in the UK levelled off towards the end of the 20th century, the industry is shifting gradually from a local scale to regional, national and international scales.

2   Environmental pressures on both inland sand and gravel extraction and large inland quarries have encouraged the aggregates industry to develop other sources of aggregate, either in remote coastal locations or offshore.

3   Stagnating demand and opposition from local and national environmental groups have delayed development of remote coastal or offshore options in the UK and Western Europe.

4   In the future, a third source of aggregate could be underground mining for crushed rock — albeit a relatively costly solution. Glensanda quarry in Scotland was designed with part of its operations underground.

5   A demand for more sustainable aggregate consumption has driven research into both the recycling of aggregates and the use of industrial wastes as secondary aggregates.

6   Recycling of industrial wastes to other uses has increased under political pressures, for instance as fuel substitutes and by addition of wastes, such as PFA, to cement and bricks.

7   Some commodities, such as sulphur and gypsum, are now produced in substantial quantities as by-products of other industrial processes.

LEARNING OUTCOMES

When you have completed this book, you should be able to explain in your own words, and use correctly, all the **bold** terms printed in the text and defined in the Glossary. You should also be able, among other things, to do the following:

Chapter 1

1.1 Outline the importance of industrial minerals through history, giving examples of notable constructions and key advances in technological developments involving industrial minerals.

1.2 Describe the global production patterns for the main industrial minerals, and the major factors influencing those patterns, while at the same time appreciating how many of these minerals are in domestic use.

Chapter 2

2.1 Describe the important properties of rocks relevant to their use as building stone, and show familiarity with specific examples of building stones.

2.2 Explain the crucial influence of transport and processing costs on the trading of building stone as a commodity at all scales, from local to international.

2.3 Outline the different methods for extracting building stones, and discuss the various options for use of abandoned quarries or underground stone mines, using examples.

Chapter 3

3.1 Describe the chemistry and origins of different types of clay, giving examples of the different types of deposit, and explain how the chemistry of some clays influences their uses.

3.2 Explain the main stages of the manufacture of bricks from clay, and outline the environmental consequences of brick-making.

3.3 Discuss UK trends in brick production and consumption during the 20th century in relation to other building materials, and outline possible uses for abandoned brick clay pits, especially landfilling.

Chapter 4

4.1 Summarize the origins, nature and UK distribution of limestones, and explain how their chemistry contributes to the manufacture of a wide range of derivative products, most importantly Portland cement.

4.2 Describe the cement-making process, and outline the impact that cement-based building materials, such as concrete, have made on the modern world.

4.3 Contrast the impact of cement-making on the environment with the wide range of environmental applications for limestone and its derivatives.

Chapter 5

5.1 Summarize the theory behind the formation of evaporite minerals, and describe the various types of mineral and deposit formed by the precipitation of salts from brines in different settings.

5.2 Outline some of the wide range of uses for the main evaporite minerals, and apply your knowledge of their chemistry to those uses, for example the formation of plaster from gypsum and the reasons for its use in fireproofing.

Chapter 6

6.1 Outline the importance of aggregates to the modern world, along with trends in their production in the UK over the last century, and discuss the changes in usage of different classes of aggregate (crushed rock, sand and gravel, and recycled aggregate).

6.2 Describe the origins of natural materials used as aggregates, their UK distribution, and explain how they are extracted and processed, exploring issues of future resource provision and land use conflicts.

6.3 Describe in detail the properties of an aggregate that determine its suitability for different uses, such as in laying a modern road and making concrete, and outline some important tests used to quantify those properties.

Chapter 7

7.1 Discuss the pressures of resource consumption, with specific reference to aggregates, and how these issues are likely to impact on society and the environment in the future.

7.2 Describe measures designed to reduce exploitation of virgin resources of industrial minerals and lead to greater sustainability, including alternative sources of useful raw materials, improved efficiency of processing and usage, and increased recycling, especially of waste materials.

REFERENCES AND FURTHER SOURCES OF INFORMATION

Manning, D. A. C. (1995) *Introduction to Industrial Minerals,* Chapman & Hall, London.

Scott, P. W. and Bristow, C. M. (2002) *Industrial Minerals and Extractive Industry Technology,* The Geological Society, Bath.

Smith, M. R. and Collis, L. (2001) *Aggregates* (3rd edn), The Geological Society, Bath.

Sheldon, P. (2005) *Earth's Physical Resources: An Introduction,* The Open University, Milton Keynes.

The topics in this book are covered, with varying degrees of accuracy, by a vast number of websites, including those of government departments; mining and quarrying companies; research institutes; universities; environmental organizations; enlightened individuals, etc. The following websites provide good information, along with links to many other sites (accessed December 2004):

British Geological Survey (BGS): http://www.bgs.ac.uk

The Geological Society of London: http://www.geolsoc.org.uk

The United States Geological Survey (USGS): http://www.usgs.gov. This website publishes *Mineral Commodity Summaries*, annual summaries of over 90 minerals and materials, with data on world production and reserves as well as brief overviews of the current issues related to each resource. These are available online at: http://minerals.usgs.gov/minerals/pubs/mcs/

The Salt Institute: http://www.saltinstitute.org/

The Quarry Products Association: http://www.qpa.org/

British Glass: http://www.britglass.co.uk/index.html

Mineral Information Institute: http://www.mii.org/commonminerals.html

Paving Expert: http://www.pavingexpert.com/. A veritable mine of information on much more than just paving — materials, techniques, standards, design — from bricks to bolsters, hoggin to hardcore, fettling to footings.

Stone Roofing Association: http://www.stoneroof.org.uk/. Informative guide to the stone slates currently in use for roofing in the British Isles, along with an overview of the Slate Industry. Includes a map of England and Wales, and the stratigraphic column.

For Open University courses on related aspects of Earth Sciences and Environment, see: http://www.open.ac.uk

ANSWERS TO QUESTIONS

Question 1.1

(a) Heat resistance, high melting-point (refractory material).

(b) Impermeability (to rain, snow); resistance to frost damage; durability.

(c) High frictional resistance to aid vehicle braking; resistance to wear.

(d) Visual impact; resistance to weathering.

Question 2.1

(a) (i) The youngest (most recent) strata are mainly in the southeast, around London and the coast of East Anglia. There are also small outcrops just west of Belfast, and near Torquay in Devon.

(ii) The southernmost outcrop of Precambrian sediments shown is the Longmynd, near Church Stretton in the Welsh Borders, which is a ridge composed of purple slates, gritstones and conglomerates.

(iii) The southernmost outcrop of intrusive igneous rock is part of a group of large granite intrusions in the southwest forming the uplands of Dartmoor, Bodmin Moor, and the Scilly Isles.

(b) London lies on rocks of Tertiary and Pleistocene age (up to 65 Ma), and Dublin on rocks of Carboniferous age (290–354 Ma), so the rocks under London will be about 250–300 Ma younger than those under Dublin. Rocks below London are described as 'clays and sands' and, being very young, are unlikely to be well cemented. The older Carboniferous 'limestones and sandstones' under Dublin are much more likely to be suitable for use as building stone.

(c) You need to measure distances on the map and convert them to kilometres using the scale provided.

(i) 65 Ma is at the *top* of the Cretaceous (65–142 Ma); it lies about 4 mm (27 km) north of London.

(ii) 290 Ma is at the *top* of the Carboniferous (290–354 Ma), about 31 mm (210 km) north of London, near Nottingham.

(iii) 443 Ma is at the *base* of the Silurian (417–443 Ma), about 73 mm (495 km) north of London, in the Southern Uplands of Scotland.

(d) There are two (bright red) outcrops of igneous rock about 400 km and 430 km north of London. These outcrops are part of a sheet of basaltic rock, the Whin Sill, which runs across the north of England to the Farne Islands. Because these rocks are intrusive, they must be *younger* than the surrounding blue Carboniferous strata. They must therefore be younger than about 290–354 Ma.

Question 2.2

(a) For a 40-tonne load of cheap crushed rock (£4 per tonne):

the quarry gate cost = $40\,\text{t} \times £4\,\text{t}^{-1} = £160$; the transport cost = £0.1 per tonne per km, which is $40\,\text{t} \times £0.1\,\text{t}^{-1}\,\text{km}^{-1} = £4$ per km per load. The transport cost will be equal to the cost of the rock,

i.e. £160, after $\dfrac{£160}{£4\,\text{km}^{-1}} = 40\,\text{km}$.

For any greater distance, transport costs would exceed quarry gate costs.

(b) Value of 10 tonnes of cheap slates = $10\,\text{t} \times £500 = £5000$ per 10-tonne load.

The transport costs are the same as for a 40 t load = $40\,\text{t} \times £0.1\,\text{t}^{-1}\,\text{km}^{-1} = £4$ per km per load. So transport costs would exceed the value at the quarry

gate after $\dfrac{£5000}{£4\,\text{km}^{-1}} = 1250\,\text{km}$.

Question 2.3

(a) Both World Wars and the Depression resulted in steep falls in the production of building stone in the USA. The magnitude of decrease was similar during the wars, but significantly larger during the Depression — after which production never regained its earlier levels.

(b) Production increased slightly in the first five years after 1950, but decreased steadily until the early 1980s, before settling into a very slow increase to 2000. Consumption followed a similar pattern, mainly at slightly higher levels, until the late 1970s. Thereafter consumption increased rapidly until 1990, suffered a minor decrease in the early 1990s, and increased steeply up to 2000.

(c) As consumption outstripped domestic USA production of dimension stone, the United States must have been importing stone from abroad. The widening gap between the two graphs indicates that imports were increasing during this period.

Question 3.1

(a) Those regions underlain by rocks older than the Carboniferous will generally lack abundant brick clay, i.e. much of Scotland, Cumbria, Wales and southwest England. Any clay rocks in these areas will have been metamorphosed, converting the original clay minerals to metamorphic minerals.

(b) Brick clay deposits in the UK occur in strata of Carboniferous age or younger (e.g. in southeast England, the Midlands, northwest and northeast England, South Wales and the Midland Valley of Scotland), and these regions also contain the main markets for bricks — the main centres of population. The implication is that these areas will have sufficient supplies of brick clay close by, while the sparsely populated northern and western highland areas will use different materials, or transport bricks a considerable distance.

Question 3.2

(a) The overall trend in demand for bricks in the UK during the second half of the 20th century was downwards — this is matched by the trend in brick production shown in Figure 3.14.

(b) It is true that light, cement-based blocks were the result of advances in *technology*, but this alone might not have resulted in substitution had bricks still been a cheaper option for building. It is the *economic* factor that drove the substitution. However, the thermal insulation standards now required would favour cement-based blocks over bricks — a technological advantage. So it is fair to say that both are correct, but that substitution was *mainly* on economic grounds.

Question 3.3

(a) Figures for UK 'commons' production (read from graph):

1960: 4700 million bricks

1990: 800 million bricks

Percentage of total UK production for commons in

$$1960 = \frac{4700 \times 10^6}{7200 \times 10^6} \times 100 = 65\%$$

Percentage of total UK production for commons in

$$1990 = \frac{800 \times 10^6}{3500 \times 10^6} \times 100 = 23\%$$

(b) (i) The actual production of facing bricks was almost identical for the two years, with a very slight increase in the number of bricks produced. Production fluctuated year by year about a roughly constant value.

(ii) Because far fewer bricks were produced in the UK in total in 1990, the *proportion* of facing bricks was much greater in 1990 ($\sim 69\%$) than in 1960 ($\sim 32\%$).

(c) Common bricks were substituted heavily by cement-based blocks in the UK during this period, whereas the use of facing bricks was hardly affected because they were retained for the outer skins of walls. This selective substitution produced the contrasting trends seen in Figure 3.14b.

Question 4.1

(a) The Chalk is soft and porous, both of which are undesirable properties for building stones that should be weather- and frost-resistant. Tough, well-cemented Carboniferous limestone has been used extensively for building, especially in the north of England within its outcrop. Some Jurassic limestones are rather porous, and weather too quickly, to be ideal building stones, but several types are sufficiently well-cemented freestones, such as Portland or Bath stone, to be widely used for civic buildings across Britain and other countries such as India and the USA.

(b) Generally, the older the limestone, the tougher and better cemented it is: rocks tend to become more lithified with time, because the *probability* that the limestone will be affected by lithifying processes (burial, compaction, fluid percolation and cementation) increases.

Question 4.2

(a) 3 months is almost 100 days, by which time the compression strength is about $40\,\text{MN}\,\text{m}^{-2}$ (Figure 4.12).

(b) According to Figure 4.12, full compressive strength of about $44\,\text{MN}\,\text{m}^{-2}$ is reached some time after 1000 days, about 3 years, and is probably nearer 5–8 years.

Question 4.3

(a) Carrara marble is the strongest material in compression, and would be favoured for this situation.

(b) Limestones are more susceptible to damage from pollution (especially acid rain) that would be more prevalent in industrial cities. Such damage could gradually weaken the structure.

Question 4.4

(a) See completed column in Table 4.8.

Table 4.8 Answer to Question 4.4a.

Material	Cost	Cost/£ t^{-1}	Density/t m^{-3}	Cost/£ m^{-3}
common bricks	£28 per 100	115	1.7	196
facing bricks	£40 per 100	172	2.0	344
handmade bricks	£45 per 100	193	1.8	347
cement blocks (= 6 bricks*)	£7.95 per m^2	61	1.3	79
lightweight blocks† (= 6 bricks*)	£8.25 per m^2	165	0.5	83
aggregate or sand	—	12	1.9	23
cement	£3.12 for 25 kg	125	not relevant	not relevant
ready-mix concrete	—	25	2.4	60

* Cement and insulating blocks occupy the same volume in a wall as 6 bricks.
† Low-density blocks used for their good insulating properties.

(b) Cement blocks are the cheapest, by the tonne, and even more so by the cubic metre (see Table 4.8). Aggregate cannot be used to make a wall, nor is concrete suitable as it requires expensive formers to hold it while it sets.

(c) Cement blocks are not necessarily the most cost effective because the better insulation from lightweight blocks (less than half the density of the normal cement blocks) will save on fuel costs in the long run and they have similar cost per m^3.

Question 5.1

Imagine a 'column' of seawater that is 1 m^2 in area by 100 m deep. It will contain 100 000 litres of water weighing 100 t, which will have dissolved in it 3.5 t (3.5%) of salts, of which 78.04% will be NaCl (Table 5.1).

Therefore, the weight of NaCl

$$= 3.5\,t \times \frac{78.04}{100} = 2.73\,t \text{ for the 1 } m^2 \text{ column.}$$

If this has a density of 2 t m^{-3}, it will form a layer

$$\frac{2.73\,t}{2\,t\,m^{-3}} = 1.36\,m \text{ thick.}$$

Similarly for gypsum, the water column will contain

$$3.5\,t \times \frac{3.48}{100} = 0.122\,t \text{ of gypsum (density 2 t } m^{-3}),$$

which will form a layer in the 1 m^2 column:

$$\frac{0.122\,t}{2\,t\,m^{-3}} = 0.061\,m \text{ thick.}$$

Question 5.2

(a) See Figure 5.11.

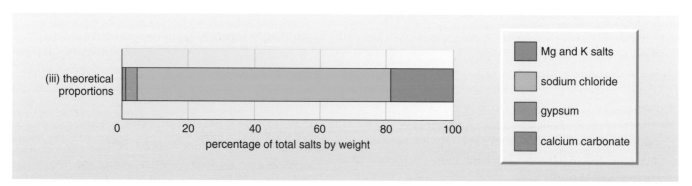

Figure 5.11   The completed Figure 5.5(iii). The amount of calcium carbonate has been exaggerated so that it can be seen; it should be only 0.33%.

(b) Gypsum is much more abundant in rows (i) and (ii) (15–25%) than in row (iii) (3.5%). This is because in nature the periods when mainly gypsum precipitates (80–90% water loss), require less extreme conditions than for formation of NaCl or Mg and K salts, and are likely to be more common (Figure 5.1). Similar reasoning expains why calcium carbonate is also more abundant in nature than in theory (row iii).

(c) Common salt, NaCl, and magnesium and potassium salts are less abundant in nature than suggested by row (iii), though the difference is minimal for NaCl between rows (i) and (iii). The reason is that all these salts will only be precipitated in the later stages of evaporation (NaCl) or when evaporation is almost complete (potassium and magnesium salts) — a very rare event in nature. Even if complete evaporation were to occur, these very soluble salts would most likely be redissolved subsequently by the next influx of the sea.

Question 5.3

(a) Estimated minimum reserves are 30 billion tonnes (3.0×10^{10} t).

Minimum lifetime of the reserves at current

extraction rates $= \dfrac{3.0 \times 10^{10} \text{ t}}{1.5 \times 10^7 \text{ t}} = 2000$ years.

(b) Percentage wastage $= \dfrac{15.0 - 8.3 \text{ Mt}}{15 \text{ Mt}} \times 100\% = 45\%$.

Question 5.4

Sugar is very *soluble* in water. So when drops of water are added to sugar a lot of sugar can dissolve. When the water evaporates, the dissolved sugar recrystallizes, cementing the grains together.

Gypsum, by contrast, is very *insoluble* in water. Table 5.1 shows that gypsum forms only about 3.48% of the 3.5% by weight of dissolved salts in seawater, so that normal seawater contains only about $3.5 \times 3.48\%$ = 0.12% of dissolved gypsum. Figure 5.1 shows that this begins to precipitate when the seawater has shrunk to 19% of its original volume. At this point, the concentration of gypsum in seawater must have increased about five times — that is, to about 0.6%. So the small percentage of water used to mix the plaster would only dissolve the minutest amount of gypsum. The mechanism for hardening the plaster cannot be dissolution and recrystallization as for the sugar, but involves the formation of hydrated calcium sulphate (gypsum) from bassanite (see Equation 5.2).

Question 6.1

In 1965 (see Figure 6.3), much more sand and gravel (100 Mt) was produced for aggregates than crushed rock (60 Mt); by 1975 production of both was between 110 Mt and 120 Mt. In 1985 the balance had shifted to 115 Mt of crushed rock, and to just over 100 Mt for sands and gravels. This gap widened as production peaked in 1989, and then fell again in the early 1990s, with > 50% more crushed rock (150 Mt) than sands and gravels (90 Mt) produced in 1991. After 1995, aggregate usage stabilized, with little change in production of either type of aggregate.

Question 6.2

There are several reasons:

- the increased demand for aggregates as more building is done with concrete;
- shortage of supply due to sterilization (building over) of sand and gravel deposits;
- environmental pressures making planning permissions more difficult;
- requirement of high-strength aggregates for advanced civil engineering projects.

Question 6.3

The slate and the porous sandstone. The slate would split into flat fragments that are the wrong shape to pack down to give a stable, low-porosity aggregate. The sandstone is very poorly cemented, with a low crushing strength, and so would not be suitable for making high-strength concrete. It is also a porous rock, likely to suffer frost damage.

Question 6.4

(a) None. It has an AAV of 14 (Table 6.6), which is acceptable for a number of low traffic-density situations. Its AIV is rather high at 23%, though below the maximum for general roadstone (35%). The real problem, however, is its PSV of 38, which is well below the minimum level of 50 for the least busy roads.

(b) With very low AAV and AIV (both 10), the only limitation will be the PSV of 66. This is acceptable for most motorway and major roads, except for the most heavily used junctions, crossings and deceleration lanes, which form a very small part of the whole road system.

Question 7.1

A quarry producing 600 000 t a year would involve 600 000/20 = 30 000 truck loads.

For 250 working days in a year, this represents 30 000/250 = 120 loads of rock each day.

But each truck must come back empty, so in an 8-hour day there will be:

$$(120 \times 2)/8 = 30 \text{ passes per hour.}$$

or, on average, one truck load every 2 minutes. No wonder local inhabitants sometimes complain.

Question 7.2

(a) Processing would probably include: sorting of the demolition rubble into suitable and unsuitable materials (for instance removing wood, plastic, slate and glass) and then further processing of the sorted rubble (i.e. crushing, screening, grading, washing etc.) to meet building specifications.

(b) Transport costs, i.e. moving the waste to and from the processing plant, to a new building site or concrete casting factory.

(c) A large contractor would be far better able to bear the direct costs and capital investment in plant to implement recycling on this scale. Some on-site reprocessing might be possible by installing plant on a large site, saving transport costs — something clearly beyond a local builder. Large projects often involve partnerships of companies, who can pool their resources to make recycling a more viable option.

Question 7.3

(a) Saving per tonne = £11 – £6 = £5

Total saving = £5 × 5364 t = £26 820*

(b) All disposal costs will be saved, including Landfill Tax. In addition, the transport costs to the landfill site will also be saved.

(c) Other possible benefits are given below:

- reduction in time needed for some of the work (e.g. from 3–4 weeks to 1 week for widening of rural roads);
- consequent reduction in road closures and thus traffic congestion;
- enhancement of Norfolk County Council's and Lafarge's environmental credentials;
- reduction in pollution from transportation of primary aggregates to site.

* These figures were based on an actual project on a country road in the UK.

ACKNOWLEDGEMENTS

Among the many people who helped in various ways during the preparation of this book, the author would particularly like to thank the following: Kip Jeffrey (University of Leicester), for copious information on a variety of industrial minerals; Malcolm Russell (Department of Trade and Industry) for supplying data on building materials; and Professor David Manning (University of Newcastle), for comments on the text and images. The author would also like to thank colleagues on the S278 Course Team (and on its predecessor, S268 *Physical Resources and Environment*) for discussions and constructive suggestions.

Grateful acknowledgement is made to the following sources for permission to reproduce material within this book:

Figure 1.2a ItaliaOnLine S.r.I; *Figure 1.2b* Ashmolean Museum; *Figure 1.2c* Paola Arosio/Diego Meozzi; *Figures 1.2d and 4.3a* copyright © Andy Sutton/ The Open University; *Figure 1.2e* copyright © 2004 Houghton Mifflin Company. All rights reserved; *Figure 1.2f* McDonald Institute for Archaeological Research; *Figure 1.3* by permission of the British Geological Survey, copyright © NERC 2001, all rights reserved; *Figure 1.4* Courtesy of Painet Inc; *Figure 1.6a* copyright © 1994 philg@mit.edu; *Figure 1.6b* Courtesy of Danny Yee; *Figure 1.6c* The National Anthropological Archives, Smithsonian Institute, picture no. 55 019; *Figure 1.6d* Courtesy of Elspeth Wales, Buro Happold; *Figures 2.1 and 2.6* by permission of the British Geological Survey, copyright © NERC, all rights reserved. IPR/56–50C and IPR/7–14; *Figure 2.4a* www.Incenseholders.com; *Figure 2.4b* www.nippon-talc.co.jp; *Figures 2.7a, b, 2.8a, 2.9b, 3.13, 3.21b, 4.3b, 4.4a, 4.13b, 4.15a, 4.16, 6.9* Dr Tom Argles, The Open University; *Figure 2.8b* Metropolitan Borough of Stockport; *Figures 2.9c(i), (ii) and (vi)* www.melocco.com.au; *Figure 2.9c(iii)* www.graniteland.com; *Figure 2.9(iv)* www.stonecontact.com; *Figure 2.9c(v)* www.granitewarehouse.com.au; *Figure 2.10* Dr Olwen Williams-Thorpe, The Open University; *Figure 2.11* 2003 Bochasanwasi Shri Aksar Purushottam Swaminarayan Sanstha; *Figure 2.13* courtesy of Mr J. Tainton; *Figure 2.15a* A. B. Hawkins; *Figure 2.16b* Hunt Midwest Enterprises; *Figures 3.1 and 3.11* Dr Naomi Williams, The Open University; *Figures 3.7, 3.16a and b* copyright © Mr Kip Jeffrey, University of Leicester; *Figure 3.9* Robert Bourgoing; *Figure 3.10a and b* Courtesy of Professor Miles Lewis, University of Melbourne; *Figures 3.10c and 6.10* copyright © John Watson, The Open University; *Figure 3.12* copyright © Guardian Newspapers Limited; *Figures 3.18 and 7.7b* copyright © Dr Andy Tindle, The Open University; *Figure 3.19a* Arizona State University; *Figure 3.19b* Reprinted with permission of The Society for Imaging Science and Technology sole copyright owners of the *Journal of Imaging Science and Technology*; *Figure 3.19c* Gordon Vrdoljak, Electron Microscope Lab, University of California, Berkeley; *Figure 3.19d* Computer Friends Inc; *Figure 3.20a* G. R. J. Browning; *Figure 3.21a* The Eden Project; *Figure 4.1c* Tom Davenport; *Figure 4.1d* Reproduced by permission of the British Geological Society. Copyright © NERC. All rights reserved. IPR/58–25C; *Figure 4.2* Wood, R. M. (1978) *On The Rocks*, BBC Publications; *Figure 4.5 (rocket inset)* NASA; *Figure 4.6a* www.johnbetts-fineminerals.com *Figure 4.6b* by permission

GLOSSARY

Items in this Glossary are printed in **bold** in the main text, usually where they are first mentioned. Terms printed in *italics* below are defined elsewhere in the Glossary.

aggregate   Natural sands, gravels and crushed rock containing fragments of varying sizes, which can be bound together — usually by *cement* or bitumen — to form constructional materials such as concrete or *asphalt*.

aggregate abrasion value (AAV)   A measure of the resistance of *wearing course aggregate* to abrasion. A low value (<14%) is desirable for road surfacing aggregate.

aggregate impact value (AIV)   A measure of the crushing strength of *aggregate*. A low value (<20%) is desirable for a road aggregate. See also *compressive strength*.

anhydrous   Term describing a substance such as a mineral that contains no water.

aquifer   A rock stratum that is sufficiently porous to store water, and permeable enough to allow water to flow through it.

asbestos   A general name for fibrous varieties of several different metamorphic minerals, mainly amphiboles, used for their fireproofing and heat-resistant properties. Inhalation of microscopic asbestos fibres generated when it is drilled or sawn can lead to cancer, and this fact led to a rapid decline in its use from about 1980 onwards.

asphalt   Fine-grained bitumen-coated *aggregate* used for the *wearing course* of roads, usually finished with high-*PSV* chippings.

asphalt planings   Materials derived mechanically from the *asphalt* layers of the *road pavement* during road maintenance.

ballast   Any *aggregate*, including gravel, but especially hard crushed rock used for *road base* or railway track; originally 'ballast' was rock imported as ship's ballast.

basecourse   Layer of bitumen-bound *aggregate* that underlies the *wearing course* in a modern tarmacadam road. Also referred to as 'binder course'.

brine   A solution of salts (especially halite, common salt) in water. Some *industrial minerals* are extracted from brines.

bund   A bank of soil and waste, which acts as a screen to quarry workings, and may be used to restore a site after extraction is finished.

cement   The powder obtained by grinding *cement clinker*. Adding water to the powder forms cement paste, which eventually sets hard, and is typically used to bind the *aggregate* in concrete. Cement may also refer to natural mineral precipitates, deposited by fluids in the pore spaces of clastic rocks, that help bind the rock particles together.

cement clinker   A hard, fused substance obtained by heating ground mudstone (often shale) and limestone together at high temperature. It is ground to produce *cement* powder.

Chalk   A fine-grained, soft, white limestone of Cretaceous age formed from the remains of planktonic organisms.

chemical sediment   A sediment composed of material precipitated from dissolved ions, by whatever process (inorganic or biochemical).

colloid   A suspension of very small (1–10 μm) particles in water, too small in size to settle as a sediment, and held in suspension partly by repulsion between negative surface charges.

compressive strength   The load (pressure) required to cause structural failure of a rock, usually measured in $MN\ m^{-2}$ or $N\ mm^{-2}$. Also termed 'crushing strength'.

crushing   The breaking down of lumps of rock into smaller fragments.

decarbonation   A chemical reaction in which carbon dioxide is expelled from the structure of a mineral, such as when calcium carbonate ($CaCO_3$) is converted to quicklime (calcium oxide, CaO).

dehydration   A reaction in which water is expelled from the structure of a mineral, such as when gypsum, $CaSO_4.2H_2O$, is converted to bassanite, $CaSO_4.\frac{1}{2}H_2O$; the reverse process is called 'rehydration'.

diapir   A vertical columnar mass of rock less dense than its surroundings that rises by its buoyancy from

MINERALS: BULK MATERIALS FOR BUILDING AND INDUSTRY

depth towards the surface, doming the overlying strata, and deforming internally. Diapirs may be of salt, mud, or granitic magma.

dimension stone   A natural stone product that has been cut or fashioned to a specified shape or size, in preparation for use in building.

dressed stone   Natural stone that has been trimmed and chiselled into the shape required for building.

drift   A British term that may be used generally for unconsolidated *superficial deposits* such as sand and gravel laid down in river systems during or since the last ice age (i.e. in the last 2 million years).

environmental impact assessment   An evaluation of the effects of an action or project on the environment, to inform planning and decision-making.

evaporite   A sedimentary rock composed of minerals precipitated during the evaporation of salty water. Such deposits consist of evaporite minerals such as halite (common salt), gypsum and potash.

fill   Material such as gravel, boulder clay or rubble (hardcore) used to level a site prior to construction work. It tends to be of local origin, and does not usually undergo any special preparation apart from compaction.

filler   A cheap, inert substance added to a product purely to increase its bulk, e.g. ground limestone which is added to plastics.

flocculation   The process in which *colloidal* particles coagulate by the neutralization of their negative surface charge; this occurs, for example, when suspended colloidal clay in rivers reaches the sea.

fluorspar   Deposits of calcium fluoride (CaF_2), when traded as a commodity; as a mineral, the same compound is known as fluorite.

flux   In industrial processes, a material that forms a low melting point mixture when added to other raw materials in a kiln or furnace. It also enables impurities to be removed in liquid form. Limestone is the flux used for iron smelting.

freestone   A rock that can equally easily be cut or split in any direction; one that has no pronounced aligned texture, bedding or 'grain'. Such rocks are well suited to be worked for building stones, or for carving.

froth flotation   A separation process that involves selective flotation of mineral grains in a frothing liquid,

whose chemical properties are adjusted so that the desired mineral is preferentially incorporated into the froth layer. The froth is then skimmed off to recover the mineral — usually a metal ore, but kaolin is also purified in this way.

geomembrane   Impervious, high-density polyethylene sheet used to seal the bottom of landfill sites.

grading envelope   Limits on a particle size distribution graph used to specify an *aggregate* for a particular application. The aggregate's cumulative frequency curve must fall within the envelope defined by these limits.

histogram   A chart of a frequency distribution, in which vertical bars are drawn with widths proportional to the intervals into which the variable has been divided, and whose heights represent the frequencies of each interval. Can be used to plot the size distribution of the grains in a sediment or an *aggregate*.

illite   A clay mineral group of general formula $KAl_2(Al,Si_3)O_{10}(OH)_2$, formed by the weathering of micas.

industrial minerals   All useful minerals and rocks that are not used as a source of metals or energy. They either have useful properties in their own right (e.g. gypsum, used in plaster) or useful non-metallic elements can be extracted from them (e.g. chlorine from common salt). Sand, gravel and crushed rock are also examples.

kaolinite   A clay mineral with the formula $Al_2Si_2O_5(OH)_4$, which is derived from the weathering of feldspars.

land bank   Proven reserves of rock for which planning permission to be worked has been granted.

landfill gas   A potentially hazardous mixture of gases, mainly methane and carbon dioxide, generated by microbiological breakdown of waste in landfill sites. Its high methane content means that it can be collected for use as fuel.

landfilling   The controlled deposition of waste on land with negligible pollution effect.

leachate   In landfill sites, a liquid formed when water is contaminated by percolation through tipped wastes.

lime   A name commonly applied to several calcium compounds, including calcium oxide or quicklime (CaO), calcium hydroxide or slaked lime ($Ca(OH)_2$), and even powdered limestone ($CaCO_3$).

lime mortar A *mortar* composed of *lime* (calcium oxide), sand, and water. It was commonly used before the re-discovery of *cement* in the late 18th century.

macadam Compacted layers of broken stone (*aggregate*) used in road-building, named after the road engineer, John McAdam. In modern roads the *aggregate* is commonly bound with bitumen to make a material known as 'tarmacadam'.

mineral liner A layer of clay used to seal the bottom of a landfill site.

mortar A mixture of *cement* with sand and water, and typically a little *lime*, which sets hard: used for laying bricks and masonry. The *cement* binder may be replaced by *lime* (see *lime mortar*).

newton (N) The standard (SI) unit of force, roughly equivalent to the force of gravity exerted on the mass of a typical apple.

oolitic Adjective describing limestone composed of concentrically layered, 0.5–2 mm rounded spheres of calcite (ooids) in calcite cement, originally formed by precipitation of calcite from warm seas. Easily worked and an attractive building stone; Bath stone, for example, is a Jurassic oolite.

overburden Material that is of little or no value and so has to be stripped off the top of a workable deposit.

overburden ratio The ratio of the thickness of waste material, the *overburden,* that has to be removed, to the thickness of the workable resource. It should be less than 1:3 for low-value materials like sand and gravel, but can be much higher (e.g. 5:1) for more valuable rocks like limestone.

oxidation A chemical process that typically involves the addition of oxygen to an element or compound, which is then said to have been oxidized. Rusting is an example of oxidation. More strictly, oxidation is defined as the removal of electrons.

place value The influence of geographical location on the price of a resource. A resource has a high place value if its location is an important factor in determining its price, especially when transport costs form a significant part of its total cost, as with cheap gravel. For polished granite slabs, however, transport costs are subordinate to the high processing costs, so they have a low place value.

plasticity The ability of a material to be shaped or formed without fracturing, as with some types of clay.

polished stone value (PSV) A measure of the resistance of *wearing course aggregate* to polishing. A high value (>60%) is desirable for road surface aggregates.

porosity The proportion of the rock volume that consists of pore space.

refractory Term describing a material that is resistant to heat, because it has a high melting point. It may also be used as a name for such materials used in high-temperature applications, such as bricks for lining blast furnaces or kilns.

residual clay A clay deposit found where it was formed by weathering of the underlying rock.

river terrace deposits More or less irregular strips of sand and gravel, at particular levels along the sides of a river valley, corresponding to remnants of the flood plain of the river in past times.

road base Layer of bitumen-bound *aggregate* that underlies the *basecourse* in a modern tarmacadam road. Also referred to simply as 'base'.

road pavement The main layers of a modern road, comprising *wearing course, basecourse, road base* and *sub-base*.

sabkha Coastal mudflats that are periodically flooded with saltwater, in which *evaporite* minerals such as halite form during the intense evaporation that follows. Sabkhas are found in arid climates.

salina An inland basin in an arid climate where *evaporite* salts crystallize, typically from a salty, ephemeral or seasonal lake.

smectite A clay mineral group with a complex chemistry, having iron and/or magnesium ions within the aluminosilicate layers as well as sodium or calcium ions, and water molecules, between those layers. Smectites are formed by the weathering of ferromagnesian minerals such as pyroxene and amphibole.

solars Artificial ponds or lagoons that are allowed to flood with *brine* (usually seawater), and which crystallize *evaporite* salts as the water evaporates. The salts are then harvested.

solution mining   The mining of soluble underground deposits (e.g. salt, potash) by pumping water down boreholes to dissolve the soluble mineral, which is then recovered from the resulting *brine* once it has been pumped back to the surface.

sorting   The extent to which minerals of different grain size are separated from one another during transport and deposition. To geologists, a 'well-sorted' sediment contains grains of similar size. To engineers, 'well-sorted' means a mixture of grain sizes, sometimes also called *well-graded material*.

sub-base   The foundation layer of a *road pavement*: comprising coarse, unbound *aggregate* laid on top of a levelled surface. It provides a stable foundation, and its high *porosity* promotes drainage.

superficial deposits   Unconsolidated sediments, which overly bedrock, such as sands and gravels laid down in river systems. May also be called *drift*.

thixotropy   The process by which a material such as bentonite clay changes from a gel to a liquid state by agitation.

till   An unconsolidated mixture of rock and mineral fragments left by melting ice. It is best described as a cobbly silt, but a common term is 'boulder clay'.

water table   The level in the Earth's crust below which cracks and voids in the rock are filled with water. It is marked by the water level in wells.

wearing course   The uppermost, bituminous layer of a modern *road pavement*, which provides the road surface. It is made from *asphalt*, with hard rock chippings rolled into the surface to increase friction. Also known as 'surface course'.

well-graded material   In construction engineering, an aggregate with a mixture of grain sizes that will compact well. See *sorting*.

INDEX

Note that **bold** page numbers refer to where terms defined in the Glossary are printed in **bold** in the text.

land bank **106**, 123–124
landfill 31, 34, 40, **54**–55, 58, 68, 130–131
    containment 56–57
    gas **55**–57, 135
Landfill Tax 55, 130, 136
larvikite 29
laterite 52
leachate **55**–57
lead 61, 73, 88, 90
Leahill, Ireland 120–121, 123
Leeds 101
legislation 54–55, 130, 132
Leicestershire 120, 125–126
Leighton Buzzard, Bedfordshire 107, 117
Leyh, Liz 69
Lias Clay 42
lightweight blocks 12, 71, 121
lightweight concrete blocks 69
lime 9, 11–12, 61, 69, **73**, 75, 77, 91
    kiln 7, 73
    mortar 7, 59, **74**, 75
limestone 5–6, 9, 11–12, 18–19, 21–25, 27, 29, 31–33, 54, 59–61, 64–66, 70, 72–75, 77, 80, 87, 89, 91, 99, 104–105, 108, 113, 116–120, 124–125, 130, 133, 135
Lincolnshire limestone 124
Lingarabay, Harris 128–130
Lion Gate, Mycenae 7
lithification 20, 24
lithium 41, 79, 90, 93
    carbonate 90
    chloride 90
    salts 82, 84, 90
load-bearing
    base 110, 114
    strength 11
Loch Aline 107
London 23–24, 27–29, 46, 102–103, 120, 126, 131, 134
London Clay 42
Long Man of Wilmington 61
lubricant 19

M

macadam **114**–116
Macchu Picchu, Peru 7
macro-friction 118
magma 5, 17
Magnesian Limestone 60–61, 64, 105
magnesium 19, 40–41, 64, 79–80
    chloride 80
    hydroxide 80, 84
    oxide 80
    salts 83, 89, 93
Maldives 60
Manchester 47, 136
manganese 90
    dioxide 45
mantle 5
marble 5, 9, 19, 24, 27, 30, 59, 61, 73
marine deposits (of sand and gravel) 102, 104, 106, 123, 125
markets 11, 14, 26, 53, 63, 66, 72, 76, 105, 107–109, 120, 123, 126, 128, 134

masonry 9, 71
McAdam, John 114
mechanical properties 9, 14
medicine 9, 19, 59, 76, 90, 92, 136–137
Mercia Mudstone 42–43, 90
mercury 9
Mesopotamia 7, 9, 14, 44
Mesozoic 22
metal
    halides 79
    ions 79
    ores 62–63
metals 5, 9, 45, 47
metamorphic rock 5, 17–22, 34, 42, 108–109, 117
metamorphism 5, 44
methane 55, 57, 73
metspar 62
Mexico 86, 90, 128
mica 17, 36–38, 52–53, 58, 96, 109, 118, 134
    schist 18
micro-friction 118
Middle Ages 28, 130
Middle East 6, 10, 14, 82, 107
Midlands 125
Millstone Grit 118–119
Milos, Greece 41
Milton Keynes 69
mineral
    deposits 81
    grains 17–18
    liner **56**
mines, mining 10, 19, 31–34, 55, 62–63, 73, 75, 84, 87, 89–91, 93, 107, 127, 129–130, 134, 136, 138
Moai, Easter Island 6
mobile elements 52
Mons Claudianus 26
mortar 7, **9**, 40, 69–71, 74, 110
mud 21, 96, 104
mud-bricks 44
mudrock 35
mudstone 5, 15, 21–22, 29, 35, 42–43, 58, 64, 84, 96
mullite 45
Mycenae, Greece 7

N

NaCl, *see* halite 10, 79
natural
    abundance 11
    aggregates 95
    stone 6, 9, 13, 15–34, 47, 69, 111
Near East 6, 14, 44
negative ions 38–39
Nene Valley, Northamptonshire 123–124
Neolithic Age 6, 9, 74
Netherlands 86, 111, 133
New Delhi 24
New Stone Age 6
Newbury, Berkshire 106
Newcastle 26, 28
newton (N) **70**
Newton, Sir Isaac 70

Nile 26
NIMBY attitude 123, 129
nitrogen 88, 135
nitrogen oxides 37
non-metallic elements 5, 46
non-reversible reactions 67
Norfolk 107, 125, 131
North Sea 83, 86
Northamptonshire 104, 123–124
Northumberland 115, 119
Norway 29
Nottingham 33
Nova Scotia 128

O

offshore deposits 102
oil 28, 35, 40–41, 63, 84–85, 90, 106–107, 137
Old Red Sandstone 22
olivine 38
ooids 59, 61
oolite 32, 59, 61, 77, 80
oolitic limestone 24, **59**
open cast extraction 129
open pits 19, 31, 41, 51, 63, 89, 91, 103–104, 107
ordinary Portland cement (OPC) 65, 67
Ordovician 20, 22, 70, 119
ore 15
    minerals 5
organic materials 6, 13
Orkney 7
ornamental stone 18, 25–26, 30, 34
Orton Scar limestone 70
overburden **104**, 108–109, 134
    ratio **104**
Oxford Clay 42–43, 50, 56, 136
oxidation **45**

P

paddock limestone 24
paint 19, 40–41, 54, 63, 75, 92–93, 107, 133, 135
Pakistan 15
Palaeozoic 22
Pantheon, Rome 7, 26, 65
paper 19, 41, 53–54, 58, 75–76, 89, 92–93
Parliament House, Adelaide 24
Parthenon, Athens, 7
particle size analysis 104, 112
Peak District 62, 73
pebbles 96, 99, 105, 113, 116
pegmatites 90
Pennines 108
Penrith sandstone 23, 45, 70
per capita consumption 111, 122
permeability 31, 45–46, 57, 106
Permian 22–23, 33, 60–61, 64, 83–84, 86, 91, 105, 108, 121
Peru 7
pesticides 40
PFA, *see* pulverized fuel ash 68
Philippines 84, 136
phosphates 137